W9-AER-702

A Passage to India

A Passage to India

a play by Santha Rama Rau

from the novel by E. M. Forster

Harcourt, Brace & World, Inc.

New York

SALEM COLLEGE LIBRARY
WINSTON-SALEM, N. C.

© 1960 by Santha Rama Rau and Edward Morgan Forster

First American edition 1961

CAUTION

Professionals and amateurs are warned that this play is subject to a royalty and must not be performed or read before an audience unless a license has been obtained in advance.

The amateur performing rights in Great Britain and the British Commonwealth (excluding Canada) are controlled by Samuel French, Ltd., of 26 Southampton Street, Strand, London. Inquiries with respect to other performing rights in these territories should be directed to Christopher Mann International, Ltd., of 140 Park Lane, London, W. 1.

Inquiries with respect to performing rights in all other territories, including the U.S. and Canada, should be directed to William Morris Agency, Inc., 1740 Broadway, New York 19, N. Y.

All rights, including professional, amateur, film, recitation, lecturing, public reading, radio, television, and the rights of translation into foreign languages, are strictly reserved.

Library of Congress Catalog Card Number: 61-8981

Printed in the United States of America

PR
6011
O 58
P38
1961

CHARACTERS

in order of appearance

DR. AZIZ, Assistant Civil Surgeon in the Government Hospital at Chandrapore

MR. FIELDING, Principal of the Government College at Chandrapore

MRS. MOORE, an elderly lady visiting her son in Chandrapore

MISS ADELA QUESTED, informally engaged to Mrs. Moore's son and travelling with her

PROFESSOR GODBOLE, Mr. Fielding's assistant at the Government College

RONNY HEASLOP, District Magistrate of Chandrapore, son of Mrs. Moore

A LIEUTENANT, stationed with the Indian Army in Chandrapore

MRS. MCBRYDE, wife of the Superintendent of Police for Chandrapore

MRS. TURTON, wife of the Collector, or Chief Administrative Officer of Chandrapore

MRS. BURTON ⎫
MRS. LESLEY ⎬ wives of other civil servants
MRS. COLLIN ⎭

MAJOR CALLENDAR, Chief Surgeon of the Government Hospital at Chandrapore

MR. BURTON ⎫ civil servants
MR. FLETCHER ⎭

MR. TURTON, the Collector of Chandrapore

MR. MCBRYDE, Superintendent of Police for Chandrapore

MRS. CALLENDAR, wife of the Chief Surgeon

MR. HAMIDULLAH, a lawyer and close friend of Dr. Aziz

MR. AMRITRAO, distinguished lawyer from Calcutta

MR. DAS, Assistant Magistrate for Chandrapore

Servants, court attendants, guards, etc.

5

61267

The action of the play takes place in the small provincial town of Chandrapore, in Eastern India, near Bengal. The time is April of a year in the early twenties.

ACT ONE

Mr. Fielding's house in the grounds of the Government College at Chandrapore, early in April at about 4 o'clock in the afternoon.

ACT TWO

Scene One A picnic site outside the Marabar Caves outside Chandrapore, at nine in the morning a couple of weeks later.

Scene Two The English Club at Chandrapore the same evening.

ACT THREE

The Magistrate's Court of Chandrapore, in the morning a couple of weeks later.

———

The play was first produced at the Playhouse, Oxford, on January 19, 1960. A provincial tour followed, after which it opened at the Comedy Theatre, London, on April 20, 1960.

ACT ONE

The scene is the living-room of Mr. Fielding's house in the grounds of the Government College of Chandrapore, India. The house was converted from an ancient garden pavilion of Moghul times. It is a peculiarly beautiful room combining a spare Muslim elegance with the warmer additions of furniture and books that Fielding's personality has imposed on it. At the back of the stage a row of graceful arches, divided by slender wooden pillars painted a soft rather romantic blue, divides the room from a formal Moghul garden designed in the conventional pattern of lily ponds and careful flower beds set in a succession of terraces, connected by shallow marble steps. In the distance an almost naked man can be seen gathering waterchestnuts from a distant tank. Throughout the ensuing act a sporadic succession of people is seen crossing the garden, an occasional woman in a bright cotton sari carrying a basket or a pot on her head, walking barefoot, easily, sometimes raising an arm to steady a load; from time to time a man in loose white pyjamas and a shirt, a bright turban, stops to exchange a few words with the man at the tank; children, perhaps, running across absorbed in some game.

One has the sensation of being simultaneously indoors and out, of no rigid separation between the garden and the room, of pale gold light filling both with a kind of impersonal disdain of the Indian

9

scene outside and the casual gesture of Westernization in the room. On Stage Right are frosted glass doors which have been put in to partition off a section of this summer-house to serve for Fielding's bedroom. Stage Left is more open. There the entrance to the house is through another archway, with a glimpse of a light, charming, rather frivolous arcade beyond. The whole thing was built in—say—the eighteenth century as a pleasure pavilion, a place to sit and view the symmetry, the formulated perfection of the view, to talk, to recite poetry, to listen to the sound of the water tumbling from pond to pond. Something of this atmosphere remains—a bare, cool floor, for instance, with a mosaic pattern in it, a fugitive fragment of stylized painting on one of the inner walls, probably a rather stiff court scene.

The furniture is too unpretentious to impress itself as an anachronism. It adds a measure of Western comfort without detracting from the atmosphere. Somewhere, on a low table, tea things are set out and covered with a large white cloth—there is always a quantity of white cloths in India, servants carry them, people wind them over their heads, hang them across their shoulders, spread them here and there—in this case because of the dust, another essential component of the Indian air. Of course there are flowers.

It is four o'clock of a Spring afternoon (in India this means the beginning of the hot weather, two or two and a half months before the monsoons, the rains of high summer, begin to cool the country again). The date is somewhere in the early twenties. The stage is empty. FIELDING's shadow can be seen crossing and re-crossing the frosted glass doors, he is apparently looking for something and is in the process of dressing in his bedroom.

DR. AZIZ *enters at Stage Left. He is a medium-sized, wiry Indian. He is full of energy—bounces slightly when he walks—he is volatile, talking quickly, expressively, with many movements of his hands. He has a sense of fantasy that leads him sometimes into ridicule and sometimes into poetry. He is formally and immaculately dressed in English clothes.*

AZIZ (*shouting cheerfully from the entrance*) Mr. Fielding! Mr. Fielding! Mr. Fielding? (*sees his shadow on the glass door*) I have simply walked in unannounced. Will you forgive this informality?

FIELDING (*from the bedroom*) Of course, of course! Please make yourself at home.

AZIZ (*takes this literally*) May I really, Mr. Fielding? It's very good of you; I like unconventional behaviour so extremely.

FIELDING I'm delighted.

AZIZ The fact is I have been wanting to meet you for a long time. But where is one to meet in a wretched hole like Chandrapore. (*with a touch of irony*) Where will the poor Indian doctor run across the Exalted European Principal of the Government College?

FIELDING My dear fellow.

AZIZ (*walks to the bedroom door*) When you first came here—I'll tell you what I used to wish. I used to wish that you would fall ill so that we could meet that way.

FIELDING *laughs.* AZIZ *joins in the laughter. He begins to improvise.*

I said to myself, "How does Mr. Fielding look this morning? Perhaps pale? And the Civil Surgeon is pale too. Malaria, without a doubt. He will not be able to attend on Mr. Fielding when the shivering commences. They will have to send for me instead."

FIELDING You know me by sight then?

11

SALEM COLLEGE LIBRARY
WINSTON-SALEM, N. C.

AZIZ Of course, of course. Not only that, but I have heard your lectures. You're a celebrated student of Persian poetry. You know me?

FIELDING I know you very well by name.

AZIZ I say, Mr. Fielding.

FIELDING Yes?

AZIZ Guess what I look like before you come out. That will be a kind of game.

FIELDING You're five feet nine inches tall——

AZIZ Jolly good!

FIELDING Well, it should be. I can see that much through the door.

AZIZ Well, what else? Have I not a venerable white beard?

FIELDING Oh blast!

AZIZ Anything is wrong?

FIELDING I've just trodden on my last back collar stud.

AZIZ Take mine, take mine.

FIELDING Have you a spare one?

AZIZ Yes, yes, one minute.

FIELDING Not if you're wearing it yourself.

AZIZ No, no, one in my pocket.

> *He steps away from the door so that* FIELDING *cannot see his outline, wrenches off his collar and pulls out the back stud, a gold one.*

Here it is!

FIELDING (*after a pause*) ·But nobody carries a spare collar stud in his pocket.

AZIZ I, always! In case of emergency.

FIELDING Nonsense.

> AZIZ *stares at the stud in his hand, dismayed. He puts it in his pocket, touchily.*

AZIZ Indians are famous for talking nonsense, doubtless you know that.

FIELDING All I meant is that I don't want to deprive you . . .

AZIZ (*sarcastically*) No depriving, rest assured. It should be the highest of honours for me.

FIELDING (*matching his sarcasm, clearly irritated*) Look, Dr. Aziz, keep your stud. I can easily send for a new one.

AZIZ By all means! Yes, yes, by all means! Send your servant to the bazaar—get your new collar stud—an unsoiled collar stud—that is what Indians are for, isn't it?

FIELDING What are you talking about?

AZIZ (*even more excited*) Only an Englishman is friend enough to do a favour. I am wrong to offer. I see that.

FIELDING (*after a long pause*) Dr. Aziz, please forgive me. Just a moment. It seems absurd to quarrel with a man one hasn't even seen. I am delighted and grateful to wear your collar stud.

AZIZ (*responding at once*) Of course, of course! No trouble!

> FIELDING *is seen tying the sash of a dressing-gown. He is wearing the trousers of his suit under the dressing-gown, socks and slippers. He is a large, shaggy man, untidy, greying, loose and easy in his movements. He smiles, shakes hands with* AZIZ, *takes the stud.*

FIELDING Many thanks. I'm ashamed of my boorishness.

AZIZ (*graciously*) Such a small thing . . .

FIELDING The fact is that my nerves are frayed. I've had a beastly day with Government inspection committees. (*he shakes his head*) Oh, God! Do sit down while I finish dressing—if you will forgive the unconventionality.

> He continues his dressing slowly through the next few minutes.

AZIZ (*looking round the bedroom inquisitively*) Very gladly. It makes me feel that we have been friends for a long time.

FIELDING Well, that may be. I've been hauled over the

coals all day about it. I'm not very popular with the higher-ups just now. They do not like unconventionality. "The British and the Indians must each keep their place," they tell me—like teams in some tiresome sort of game.

AZIZ Don't Englishmen like sports?

FIELDING (*laughing*) I can't be bothered with that sort when I'm trying to get my work done. However, I'm sure you didn't come here to listen to my troubles. Do sit down.

AZIZ (*enthralled with the room*) But I always thought Englishmen kept their rooms so tidy. It seems this is not so. I need not be so ashamed.

> *He sits down gaily on the sofa, and forgetting himself entirely, draws his legs up under him.*

Everything ranged coldly on shelves was what I thought. Shall I tell you something, Mr. Fielding? This is the first time I have ever been invited to an Englishman's house. Sometimes I have been summoned in case of sickness when my superior Major Callendar is away. But for a jolly social occasion like this—informal, as equals—never. No, no, never, never.

FIELDING (*looking at him intensely*) Really? How—how astonishing.

AZIZ Yes, really. But not astonishing. For I am not a bootlicker. I am not one of those.

FIELDING I don't mean that. I mean that there seem to be no bounds to our stupidity in India. Why must we add social insult to political injury, I wonder?

AZIZ Very good! Very good, Mr. Fielding. Social insult to political injury. I shall remember that to tell my friends.

FIELDING It can't be a new idea to them, surely.

AZIZ The idea, no. But to hear it from an Englishman, yes. Let me assure you, oh yes. We talk such things among ourselves, my friends, and I——

14

FIELDING   However, if it's all the same to you, I'd appreciate it if you didn't mention that remark to them. It was just—just a casual observation.

AZIZ   And a true one. If you so wish, I shall not mention. But—forgive the following question, Mr. Fielding—may I ask why?

FIELDING   Oh, no particular reason. It's just that there's really no point in making trouble. I'm in enough hot water as it is.

AZIZ (*touchy again*)   You are worried about the indiscretion of my friends?

FIELDING (*uncomfortably*)   No, no, of course not. (*meaning, "Yes, perhaps."*)

AZIZ   Indians, too, understand discretion. That is not reserved only for the British.

FIELDING   Come, come, Aziz, I wasn't insulting your friends.

AZIZ   That is good, for they are very big-hearted chaps. You know old Hámidullah, the lawyer? Or Mahmoud Ali—ah, there's a philosopher!—or the Nawab Bahadur? Perhaps you have never heard of them?

FIELDING   I've heard of them. I suppose none of you ever go to the Bridge parties?

AZIZ   As Muslims, Mr. Fielding, we do not play cards.

FIELDING   I'm sorry—it's not that kind of bridge. The Bridge is one of Turton's depressing little jokes—he means a party to bridge the gulf between East and West.

AZIZ   Ah, I see. A Bridge party. Very witty.

FIELDING *nods.*

No, we never go to those. My friends say to me, "What can we expect from these English? Scorn, no understanding of our customs and our civilization—social insults, you see—Better leave them alone."

FIELDING   They may very well be right, you know.

AZIZ   No, Mr. Fielding. Excuse me, I must disagree. You see, I think friendship is possible—not only possible but important. Yes, yes, I know what you will tell me—my

15

friends tell me the same—oil and water, we do not mix. We have our political differences. You do not like our food and our customs and we try to like yours, but—(*he shrugs*) In any event, you think us backward, we find you uncouth. What to do? I say there must be friendship. Nothing will shake me in that idea. Nothing, Mr. Fielding! Nothing! I say that the friendship between two individuals is bigger than all those other things. You agree?

FIELDING Well, I never heard of any friendships that began at those Bridge parties.

AZIZ My friends are wise when they advise me not to go—though imagine, I might have met *you* there, Mr. Fielding. Also I am curious about the English Club where we may not enter.

FIELDING (*laughing*) You would find it excessively boring —billiards, tennis, shop talk in the smoking-room, drinks in the bar where Englishmen don't mind having a few too many since there are no Indians to observe them. It's quite deadly really.

AZIZ Then why do you go?

FIELDING Oh, I don't know. If I didn't I suppose people would think me peculiar, and I have found that it is simpler not to make enemies—they take up too much time.

AZIZ Or friends either? They, too, take up time? You bring tears to my eyes, Mr. Fielding! Such a lonely life as you describe! Shall I tell you something else? This is a Persian poem that I shall have inscribed on my tomb when I die! Please listen.

>"Alas without me for thousands of years
>The Rose will blossom and the Spring will bloom
>But those who have secretly understood my heart—
>They will approach and visit the grave where I lie."

Is that not beautiful? Is it not profound philosophy? That, you see, is what I want . . . the secret understanding of the heart!

FIELDING (*smiling*) I am not so ambitious. I only want to teach—particularly here—I can't complicate my life with things that would interfere with that.

AZIZ If I were so good as you in my profession——

FIELDING You flatter me.

AZIZ No flattery! I assure you! I have heard your lectures.

FIELDING Why the hell do we wear collars?

AZIZ *works on the stud.*

AZIZ We wear them to pass the police.

FIELDING (*ready to laugh*) What?

AZIZ If I'm biking in English dress . . . (*pantomiming*) starch collar, hat with ditch—they take no notice. When I wear a fez, they cry, "Your lamp's out." Let me put that in, Mr. Fielding. Lord Curzon did not consider this when he asked natives of India to retain their picturesque costumes—Hooray! Stud's gone in.—Sometimes I shut my eyes and dream I have splendid clothes again and I'm riding into battle behind Alamgir. The Moghul Empire at its height and Alamgir reigning at Delhi upon the Peacock Throne. Mr. Fielding, don't you think India must have been beautiful then?

FIELDING I do indeed. Well, you will have an opportunity to describe it all to the two ladies who are coming to tea to meet you—I think you know them.

AZIZ Meet me? I know no ladies.

FIELDING Really? Not Mrs. Moore and Miss Quested?

AZIZ Oh yes—I remember. Mrs. Moore. An excessively aged lady. But will you please repeat the name of her companion?

FIELDING Miss Quested. You can tell her about the Peacock Throne if you like. She's a Kensington intellectual. (*very gently mocking*) She tells me she wants to know the *real* India.

AZIZ I see.

FIELDING She was saying the other night at the Club that she was tired of seeing picturesque Indians pass before her as a frieze, that now she wanted to meet some of them.

AZIZ (*disappointed*) So this is to be a Bridge party after all.

FIELDING (*quickly*) Oh no—please forgive me. I have made Miss Quested sound a prig—which is not at all what I intended. I thought it very sensible of her to want to meet Indians. If she's really going to make her life in this country.

AZIZ Ah, now I see.

> *Significantly, for he has taken* FIELDING's *remark to mean that* MISS QUESTED *will make her life with* FIELDING *himself.*

She is to settle here in Chandrapore altogether?

FIELDING Well, one doesn't know yet for sure. She may be getting married here.

AZIZ (*sincerely*) I am honoured that you tell me this on such short acquaintance. I mean this most sincerely. And without doubt I will attempt to entertain her in my poor way.

FIELDING (*he hasn't caught* AZIZ's *assumption*) Well, that's very good of you. But actually, she's not the reason why I invited you this afternoon. Mrs. Moore, who has chaperoned her on this trip to India, told me that she knew you and wanted very much to see you again. She asked me particularly to invite you. So naturally, I agreed.

AZIZ (*offended that it hasn't been* FIELDING's *own idea*) Naturally. The ladies must have their wish. Though I cannot imagine why Mrs. Moore should have asked since I don't really consider that I know her. I only met her accidentally in my mosque. I had gone there one night, alone, for a moment of rest and meditation. She moved in the darkness and I thought she was a ghost. I daresay I frightened her, too, for when I saw in the moonlight that it was a European woman I shouted out,

"Madam, madam, madam! This is a holy place for Muslims. You must take your shoes off."

FIELDING And did she?

AZIZ (*his good humour restored by the recollection*) She couldn't. She had already taken them off and left them in the entrance in the correct way. It is remarkable, is it not, that she should have taken the trouble? So few European ladies would, especially if thinking no one is there to see.

FIELDING Did you tell her that?

AZIZ Oh yes. And she replied in poetry. She said, "That makes no difference. God is here." Poetry, you see. Afterwards we talked about her children and mine.

FIELDING So you are friends after all.

AZIZ Oh yes. I know Mrs. Moore well. She is a great friend of mine, and besides, she is an oriental.

FIELDING How do you mean?

AZIZ She told me she didn't understand people very well, but she knew how to like or dislike them.

FIELDING So that's oriental. I wonder if my assistant, Godbole, would agree with that definition. He's supposed to be coming to tea today, too. We must ask him this afternoon. If he shows up, that is.

AZIZ Why should he not show up? All Indians are not so unreliable. And for the honour of taking tea with the Principal?

FIELDING I don't know how much of an honour it is. When I have asked him he has always found some excuse on previous occasions.

AZIZ Ah, the good professor is no doubt too much in awe of you, Mr. Fielding.

FIELDING More likely, he finds my food unclean and is too polite to say so. He is orthodox, you know.

AZIZ Oh yes. Such Brahmins are very strict. All are immensely subtle. Hindu philosophy is too much for me. We poor Muslims, we rely on our heart, not so much on our intellect. The feelings of our heart will lead us to God, do you not agree?

FIELDING Well, we are taught that God is love, but I have never——

AZIZ You see? You see? We are brothers after all, Mr. Fielding.

FIELDING (*laughing*) My dear chap! I can't keep up with you—you make my head swim!

AZIZ (*laughing with him*) That is very good—it is the first step. Taking to another element, we will swim together and so become friends!

> *A* SERVANT *enters from Stage Left and stands in the archway. Immediately behind him are* MRS. MOORE, *an elderly grey-haired woman with a rather absent manner, and* MISS QUESTED, *a thin blondish young woman in her late twenties. She has a vigorous, enquiring way about her, verging sometimes on nervousness. She is certainly intelligent and culti-vated and to Western eyes not unattractive. To Indians she would seem pitifully ugly—the freckles, the colourless hair, the flattish chest, the lack of grace and feminine modesty. A beautiful woman might have troubled* AZIZ *but because* MRS. MOORE *seemed to him so old and* MISS QUESTED *so plain, his manner to both remains easy and straightforward.*

FIELDING (*walking across the room to escort the women from the door*) Good afternoon, good afternoon. You had no trouble finding the way?

QUESTED None at all. Mr. Heaslop sent us in his carriage. He'll be coming later to take us back.

AZIZ (*buoyantly from across the room*) Oh what a pleasure to see Mr. Heaslop later on. If he comes to fetch you, indeed you are in good hands.

> MISS QUESTED *looks at him rather startled by his tone, for he is talking about her fiancé.* FIELDING *quickly begins introductions.*

FIELDING   Mrs. Moore, I believe that you and Dr. Aziz have already met.

MOORE   Yes indeed. How nice to see you again!

AZIZ *walks to the group by the archway to shake hands.*

FIELDING   Miss Quested, Dr. Aziz.

MISS QUESTED *smiles in recognition of the name—* MRS. MOORE *has mentioned the incident in the mosque. She moves with* AZIZ *to the sofa while* MRS. MOORE *finds a straight-back chair and* FIELDING *mutters instructions to the* SERVANT *about tea.*

QUESTED   Dr. Aziz, I am especially pleased to meet you. I feel that perhaps you can help me to *understand* India.

AZIZ   Who understands India? Not the Indians, at least.

FIELDING   Now won't you all sit down?

QUESTED   I heard from Mrs. Moore how kind you were to her in the mosque, and how interesting. She learned more about India in those few minutes' talk with you than in the three weeks since we landed.

AZIZ   Oh please do not mention a little thing like that. Is there anything else I may tell you about my country?

QUESTED   A disappointment we had this morning; I wonder if you could explain, of course it may be some form of Indian etiquette.

AZIZ   There is no question of etiquette. We are by nature a most informal people.

An astonished silence from the others greets this remark. AZIZ *is unaware of it.* FIELDING *starts to say something but is gently interrupted.*

MOORE   I was afraid we had blundered and given offence.

AZIZ   That is even more impossible. But may I know the facts?

QUESTED   An Indian lady and gentleman had invited us to call on them and were to send their carriage for us this morning at nine. It has never come. We waited and waited and waited.

FIELDING (*trying to smooth the matter over*) Some misunderstanding, I'm sure.

QUESTED Oh no, it wasn't that. They even put off going to Calcutta to entertain us.

FIELDING I wouldn't worry about it, anyway.

QUESTED (*a little heatedly*) That's exactly what everyone tells me. But if one doesn't worry, how is one ever going to *understand*?

AZIZ I think they were ashamed of their house and that is why they did not send.

FIELDING That's very possible.

QUESTED I do so hate mysteries.

FIELDING Very English of you.

QUESTED I dislike them not because I'm English, but— from a personal point of view.

MOORE (*interrupting vaguely*) I like mysteries, but I rather dislike muddles.

FIELDING A mystery is a muddle.

MOORE (*unemphatically*) Oh, do you think so, Mr. Fielding?

FIELDING Well, a mystery is a high-sounding word for a muddle. Aziz and I know that India's a muddle.

MOORE India—Oh what an alarming idea!

AZIZ (*who has been listening to this exchange in some bewilderment, moving his head from side to side as if he were at a tennis match*) There'll be no muddle when you come to visit me in my house. Mrs. Moore and everyone—I invite you all—oh please.

MOORE That is most kind of you, Dr. Aziz. I shall be delighted.

QUESTED I too! (*she produces a small book from her purse*) May I write down the address?

AZIZ (*horrified—they have taken a moment of politeness seriously*) How sad that my bungalow is terrible! It is near the bazaar. There is no room at all, and even that is infested with small black flies. Oh, but we will talk of something else now. See this beautiful room! See those curves at the bottom of the arches. What delicacy! It is the architecture of Question and Answer. Mrs. Moore, you are in *India*; I am not joking. Imagine—now, imagine I am some high official of the eighteenth century. This is my audience hall. I am doing justice here. A poor widow who has been robbed comes to me and I give her fifty rupees. To another, with some different complaint, I give a hundred—I should like that.

MOORE (*smiling*)   Rupees don't last forever. But I agree, the modern method does seem to lack imagination—or humanity. But rupees don't last forever.

AZIZ   My rupees would last. God would give me more when He saw that I gave.

QUESTED   I had thought that our penal code was one of our more successful achievements in India. Mr. Heaslop has explained to me that there was no comprehensive system of justice for all of India before the British rule.

AZIZ   Justice? Oh, Miss Quested, you speak of something else. Yes, yes, I agree the British official can administer the law, but it takes a Prince to give the people justice. Oh, indeed yes, (*for he sees a doubtful look on* MISS QUESTED's *face*) because justice is giving, always giving, always kindness and more giving. I think we would never punish anyone.

> FIELDING *is busy serving tea.* MRS. MOORE *smiles and nods her agreement and pleasure in* AZIZ. MISS QUESTED *listens intently, trying hard to understand this foreign point of view.*

MOORE   How different from my son's conception of being a magistrate!

QUESTED   But, Dr. Aziz—is there a satisfactory alternative to the punishment of criminals? You see, in England I served on a committee for the improvement of prison conditions and of course——

AZIZ (*interrupting buoyantly*)   Poor criminal! Give him

23

another chance! It only makes a man worse to go to prison and be corrupted. We punish no one, no one in my palace and in the evening we will give a great banquet with a nautch and lovely girls shall shine on every side of the tank with fireworks in their hands, and all shall be feasting and happiness until the next day, when there shall be justice as before . . . fifty rupees, a hundred, a thousand . . . till peace comes. Ah, why didn't we live in that time? . . .

MOORE (*laughing*) But India is still beautiful, think of our mosque.

AZIZ Mrs. Moore, do you remember our mosque?

MOORE Of course.

AZIZ Do you remember how we saw the moon caught in the tank of water? Trembling and bigger than the real moon? Do you remember?

MOORE I will never forget it.

AZIZ Do you know that the water comes down from our mosque and fills the garden in Mr. Fielding's house? A skilful arrangement of our Emperors. They loved water. Wherever they went they created fountains, gardens, hammams——

QUESTED (*producing her little notebook in which she writes down the foreign words as she comes across them*) What was that? Hammams? How do you spell that, please?

AZIZ A hammam is a bath . . . but oh, Miss Quested, it is a beautiful luxurious bath. Imagine yourself a princess, Miss Quested, your black hair flowing down to your waist, polished and shining like the wing of a bird, face is round like the moon, breasts like pomegranates. You are surrounded by your handmaidens who rub your skin with sandalwood oil, and perfume the water of the hammam with musk, and then scatter over it rose petals for beauty. Somewhere in the garden a bul-bul is singing. Oh, there is no sweeter sound than the bul-bul. You step out of your veils and into the water, and——

FIELDING *clears his throat noisily, half-smiling at the weird contrast between the straight-backed, unvoluptuous figure of* MISS QUESTED *and* AZIZ's *description.*

FIELDING Aziz, give Mrs. Moore another cup of tea, please.

AZIZ A pleasure, a pleasure. (*he fills her cup*) And Miss Quested too.

QUESTED Oh yes, please.

AZIZ (*he takes the pot over to her and as he pours says*) Pretend that this is sherbet you are drinking . . . the drink of those beautiful, voluptuous princesses . . .

MISS QUESTED, *uncomfortable and alarmed by* AZIZ's *extravagance, looks up at him as he speaks, bending over her. Her hand trembles and the tea spills over her dress and the sofa. She jumps up, the cup shatters.*

QUESTED Oh, I am sorry . . . look what I've done . . . oh dear . . .

FIELDING It doesn't matter a bit. (*shouts*) Ranjit!

The SERVANT *appears to clean up the mess.*

QUESTED Oh, I *am* so sorry . . . I don't know what got into me . . .

AZIZ Miss Quested, shall I tell you what we say? We say that to spill food or drink is the sign of a generous heart, full to overflowing, you see.

FIELDING *looks at him gratefully and makes an indication of a Muslim salaam.* AZIZ *returns it, smiling.*

QUESTED (*more at ease now*) That makes me feel better. (*to* FIELDING) Oh, I hope I haven't ruined your sofa. I am not usually so clumsy.

FIELDING As Aziz says, not clumsiness, only generosity of spirit.

He is laughing.

QUESTED (*laughing too*) Well, at least I have learned this afternoon how to make a virtue out of an ineptitude.

> GODBOLE *enters. He is middle-aged, erect, dressed in Indian clothes, a large red and yellow caste mark on his forehead. He is polite, enigmatic. He does not shake hands, but brings the palms together in a namaskar . . . the Indian greeting.*

FIELDING Ah Godbole, I've got you here at last. You already know Aziz. Here are two new visitors to Chandrapore. Mrs. Moore, Miss Quested. My elusive assistant, Professor Godbole.

> MRS. MOORE *nods to* GODBOLE. MISS QUESTED *rather awkwardly copies Godbole's namaskar.*

Mrs. Moore, as I expect you know, is the mother of our City Magistrate.

AZIZ Of Mr. Heaslop? Mrs. Moore, how can that be?

MOORE My first husband, Ronny's father, died.

AZIZ And Moore? Who is Moore?

MOORE I married again. It is not considered extraordinary in England.

AZIZ I see. I see. Well, then, Mrs. Moore we are in the same box. My wife is dead also. Now we have only our children. My children are the greatest joy to me. Yours too, Mrs. Moore?

MOORE A joy and an anxiety.

AZIZ (*rather naughtily*) Alas for poor Mr. Fielding, he has no children! Neither the joys nor the anxieties! Does that not give you the cause for concern, Mr. Fielding?

FIELDING Not in the least.

AZIZ This indifference is what the Oriental will never understand. Just think—your name will die out entirely——

FIELDING I suppose so (*laughing*)—unless, of course, I do get married after all.

AZIZ (*delightedly*) It is still possible! I know, I know! And allow me to wish you much happiness in advance.

GODBOLE And I will send you up some few healthy sweets on that occasion. I will give myself that pleasure.

AZIZ I tell you what, Mr. Fielding, we will make your visit to me a celebration . . . a celebration in advance . . . that is the best kind!

FIELDING Nothing elaborate when we come to visit you. (*to the ladies*) Isn't that so?

QUESTED Oh, of course. Please don't disarrange your household.

AZIZ Not in my house—it is too dreadful!

GODBOLE The house is but a shell. Inside, the living creature.

AZIZ But Professor, this creature would be dead of shame. I know what! I invite you all to visit me in the Marabar Caves. When I return to Chandrapore, that is.

MOORE You are going away, Dr. Aziz?

AZIZ A brief visit, no more, to a relative in Calcutta. (*laughing*) He has so many daughters he needs some masculine conversation!

QUESTED Well, when you get back, then?

AZIZ Indeed! Please do not forget . . . we picnic in the Marabar Caves.

FIELDING Excellent.

AZIZ Godbole, you will join us?

GODBOLE Oh, that is a most magnificent entertainment! But have not the ladies already visited our caves?

QUESTED No, I've not even heard of them.

AZIZ Not *heard* of them? The Marabar Caves in the Marabar Hills? Why they are one of the greatest wonders of the world.

QUESTED I'm sure that someone like you, Dr. Aziz, who has seen them so often will find me foolish . . . but tell me what I should look for when I get there.

AZIZ Unfortunately, I have never visited the caves myself. Work or private business has prevented me, and besides they are very far away.

FIELDING (*laughing*) My dear Aziz!

QUESTED Professor Godbole, you have seen the Caves? (*he nods*) Let me ask, are they large caves?

GODBOLE No, not large.

MOORE Do describe them, Professor Godbole.

GODBOLE It will be a great honour. (*longish pause*) There is an entrance in the rock . . . Which you enter . . . And through the entrance is the cave.

FIELDING Something like the caves at Elephanta?

GODBOLE Oh no, not at all. At Elephanta there are sculptures of Siva and Parvati. There are no sculptures at Marabar.

AZIZ They are immensely holy, no doubt?

GODBOLE Oh no, oh no.

FIELDING Ornamented in some way?

GODBOLE Oh no.

AZIZ Why do we talk so much about the Marabar Caves? Perhaps that is our empty brag.

GODBOLE No, I should not quite say that.

AZIZ Then they *are* deservedly famous? Yes?

GODBOLE Oh yes, famous with reason. And terrible . . . with reason?

QUESTED Terrible? But how can a cave be terrible? Especially when there is nothing there.

GODBOLE Miss Quested, pardon me, there is everything there. For in nothing, there is all.

QUESTED I'm sorry, I'm not sure that I understand you. Is it the emptiness that is terrible?

GODBOLE Ah, if it were a question of emptiness, then, indeed, the caves would be empty and nobody would go there. Why would they become famous, in such a case? In our religion, in Hinduism, you see, everything has two or many faces. In the terror there is also calm and comfort. The Creator is also the destroyer. Kali, Parvati, Durga, Uma are equally consorts of Shiva.

QUESTED I thought you said there were no carvings there?

GODBOLE There are none.

28

MOORE (*vaguely*) Adela doesn't believe in ghosts. She only believes the evidence of her eyes.

QUESTED Well, there must be *something* to see.

GODBOLE There is enlightenment or obscurity. Nothing to see except with the inner eye. Therefore I would advise you to choose some other environs for your picnic.

AZIZ For *our* picnic, Godbole. Surely you will not refuse my invitation.

GODBOLE I am honoured to accept.

QUESTED Then, at least *you* are not afraid, Professor? I must say you have piqued my curiosity to a point where it must be satisfied. Do let us make the appointment definite.

GODBOLE By all means. I have no doubt that you will find the Caves very beautiful.

AZIZ Excellent. Then, Professor, describe their beauties to these ladies, please.

GODBOLE It will be a pleasure. (*a longish pause while* GODBOLE *thinks*) However, I think I will forgo the pleasure.

FIELDING (*to break an awkward silence*) Mrs. Moore, would you like to see our College gardens? We are rather proud of them.

MOORE Thank you. I am very fond of gardens . . . I find that they repay love in a way that human beings very often do not.

FIELDING *looks to* MISS QUESTED *to join them.*

QUESTED I'll stay here if I may and talk to Professor Godbole and Dr. Aziz. This is such a rare and valuable opportunity for me.

MRS. MOORE *and* FIELDING *leave through the garden.* MISS QUESTED *settles back on the sofa and to the scarcely concealed astonishment of the Indians, lights a cigarette. She doesn't notice their embarrassment.*

QUESTED Do you know, this is the very first time that I've had a chance to talk to Indians since I've been in this country? At the Club, where we usually go of an evening, people never seem to mention India or Indians. I don't know what happens to them—the Callendars, the McBrydes——

AZIZ   The Turtons and the Burtons . . .

QUESTED   Well, I'm sure they're all reasonable people in England. But somehow, when they get to India . . . they become . . . I don't know . . .

AZIZ   Unkind?

QUESTED   They become insensitive, certainly . . .

GODBOLE   They have, perhaps, lost one reality, and have not yet found another?

QUESTED (*puzzled*)   That may be true . . . But the odd thing is that they don't seem to be even *interested* in India— and I feel that we can only be of some good here if we have . . . well, a very different attitude.

AZIZ   Oh, I agree . . . such as Mr. Fielding's attitude. He understands poor Indian. Godbole will bear out that fact, isn't it?

GODBOLE   Yes, yes. He makes fine principal of Government College, Chandrapore. A very impartial man.

QUESTED   Yes, I am sure he is. But you see the thing that is really worrying me . . . I mean, if I *were* to settle in India—for whatever reason . . . I mean, if I *had* a reason to stay on, what could I do? What would be the most *useful* thing for India? Is that a foolish question, Professor Godbole?

GODBOLE   Not foolish. No, no. In our ancient Sanskrit writing, *Bhagavad-gita* we are told, "Even the wise are perplexed as to what is action and what is inaction." Not at all foolish.

QUESTED   Then can you help me with the answer?

GODBOLE   Ah yes. Use and abuse are the same in the end.

QUESTED   The *same?*

GODBOLE   Without self-knowledge.

QUESTED *shakes her head confusedly and looks enquiringly at* AZIZ.

30

AZIZ (*warm and earnest. He jumps up to sit next to* MISS QUESTED *on the sofa*) In any case, why be useful, Miss Quested? Just love India. That is the greatest gift.

QUESTED (*shifting nervously deep into her corner of the sofa*) No, but I'm serious, Dr. Aziz. In England I'm used to leading an active life . . . so different from the kind of life the English wives lead out here.

GODBOLE To love is very active. It can take all your life . . . if you accept fully all its meanings.

QUESTED (*smiling indulgently at* GODBOLE, *but looking immediately back at* AZIZ) Professor, you are probably right, but I'm not a philosopher. I need something less abstract . . .

AZIZ (*gaily*) Miss Quested, I tell you what. Think with your heart for this time, not your head. Heart! Heart, I say!

> MISS QUESTED *gets up suddenly and almost involuntarily, then she has to look for a pretext . . . she puts out her cigarette, and carefully chooses a chair across the room from* AZIZ *in which to sit.*

QUESTED (*getting herself under control*) But . . . but that's just . . . just what I can't do. (*with spirit*) What's the point of having a brain if one doesn't use it? I intend to use mine to understand what I can about India and then to put that knowledge to some good.

AZIZ But you'll never understand without your heart . . .

QUESTED And I think I'll never understand with it. (*with some antagonism*) Perhaps that is the difference between Orientals and Westerners.

AZIZ But Mrs. Moore feels . . . with her mind, too.

QUESTED Dr. Aziz, I'm sorry. I don't mean to criticize— but I can't agree with the Oriental idea of women . . . that we mustn't use our minds. That we should be just wives and mothers . . .

GODBOLE There is a higher ideal, perhaps?

QUESTED Oh, Professor! Oh yes! At least, I think so. Mrs.

Moore belongs to another generation . . . things were different in her day . . .

AZIZ (*coldly*) How difficult to explain this to Indians!

QUESTED (*rather nastily*) I can see that men might not wish to relinquish their privileges.

AZIZ Where there is heart, privilege does not matter. The English have many privileges in India . . .

QUESTED And no feelings? Is that what you are saying?

AZIZ I have no wish to find fault.

QUESTED (*slightly heated*) But you must! You must! Civilized people can discuss things without getting heated, surely. That's what I *want*!

AZIZ And what I want, Miss Quested, is only that you should enjoy yourself in India.

QUESTED (*getting worked up and disturbed*) Oh, picnics—and enjoyment—of course they're part of one's life . . . but my real worry is this: if I *did* stay in India, for a long time, that is . . . I might simply become another idle Englishwoman—what you call an Anglo-Indian.

GODBOLE Oh never, Miss Quested. You would always be too thoughtful.

QUESTED I'm told we all get thoughtless after a year. I know I can't . . . I mean, *couldn't* . . . avoid the label. What I should hope to avoid is the mentality. I feel that any modern, educated person has a duty to the community in which he lives, India, that is. So you see, enjoyment just isn't enough . . .

AZIZ It is everything——

QUESTED (*more heated*) Life is more than frivolity . . .

AZIZ (*equally heated*) I'm talking about enjoyment . . . giving yourself to your feelings . . .

QUESTED But Dr. Aziz——

AZIZ Without it, Miss Quested, please understand me . . . without it you will never love India and Indians will never love you . . .

QUESTED Love? (*a shocked silence*) Well—I only meant

that I hoped I would get along and be able to do some good.

AZIZ (*indifferently*) I see that my idea of a picnic has not pleased you. Perhaps we should think of some other, more suitable entertainment.

QUESTED (*penitent and concerned. She walks over to him*) Oh please, Dr. Aziz—please, I hope I haven't offended you. I . . . it's just that India is so big and difficult to grasp, and I have so many decisions to make . . .

AZIZ (*smiling*) I wish you good fortune with your "decision".

QUESTED I must hold on to the best and the most rational part of me . . .

GODBOLE We learn to protect ourselves when we learn we have something to fear.

> GODBOLE *smiles and nods. From the garden a voice is heard calling "Hallo! Hall-o!"* RONNY HEASLOP *enters from the garden, and pauses under the blue arches looking around at the room and its occupants. He is an extremely good looking man and that justifies a lot of his insensitivity to a girl like* MISS QUESTED *who hovers on the edge of intellectuality.*

HEASLOP (*in annoyance*) Well, here you are. What's happened to Fielding? Where's my mother?

> *The* INDIANS *have stood up, but he doesn't look at them.*

QUESTED (*coolly*) Good evening, Ronny.

HEASLOP I want you and mother at once. There's to be polo.

QUESTED I thought there was to be no polo.

HEASLOP Everything's altered. Come along, and I'll tell you all about it.

AZIZ Good evening, Mr. Heaslop.

GODBOLE Your mother will return shortly, sir. There is but little to see in our poor college.

HEASLOP (*paying no attention to the* INDIANS) We must hurry, my dear. (*looks around*) Perhaps I should send a servant to find my mother.

QUESTED (*still cold*) Surely we shouldn't leave like this.

AZIZ (*with rather offensive friendliness, pats* HEASLOP *on the arm*) Come along in and join us, Mr. Heaslop; sit down until your mother turns up.

HEASLOP (*turning away*) Boy! Boy! (*a pause*) What's the matter with Fielding's servants? Have they all decided to take a holiday? I dare say they're loafing in their quarters, drinking tea . . . Boy! Boy!

> AZIZ *steps forward about to say something angrily.* GODBOLE *puts a hand on his arm and stops him.*

GODBOLE (*gently*) Please allow us the honour, sir, of fetching Mrs. Moore and Mr. Fielding for you.

> *He leads* AZIZ *away and* MISS QUESTED *watches them until they are out of hearing.*

QUESTED (*turning sharply to* HEASLOP) Ronny, I'm appalled . . .

HEASLOP As well you might be. I'm appalled too, I don't know what's come over Fielding.

QUESTED Mr. Fielding? What has *he* done?

HEASLOP Well . . . I'm the sun-dried bureaucrat, no doubt; still I don't like to see an English girl left smoking cigarettes with two Indians.

QUESTED This particular English girl stayed here, as she smokes, by her own wish.

HEASLOP Yes, that's all very well in England.

QUESTED I really can't see the difference . . . or the harm.

HEASLOP If you can't see, you can't see . . . Can't you at least see that fellow's a bounder?

QUESTED He isn't a bounder. He just got nervous, that's all.

HEASLOP What could have upset his precious nerves?

QUESTED (*trying to bring the disturbing ideas* AZIZ *has suggested safely down to an ordinary level*) I don't know.

He was all right until you arrived. In fact he was very
. . . interesting.

HEASLOP (*cheerfully*) Well, it's nothing I've said. I never
even spoke to him.

QUESTED (*turning away in exasperation*) O Ronny . . . it's
just impossible.

HEASLOP Nothing's impossible, only difficult. Don't worry,
everyone's temper gets short during this heat.

QUESTED But this has nothing to do with the weather.

HEASLOP Everything has something to do with the weather
in India. But don't fret—after we're married you won't
have to suffer through it again, I promise you. I'll pack
you off to the hills every April . . . I'm not one to keep
a wife grilling in the plains.

QUESTED Really, it isn't *that*. I have a sudden . . . sort of
vision of what life here would be . . . the Club in the
evenings, the Hills in the hot weather.

HEASLOP It's not a bad life as long as we do our work and
keep to ourselves.

QUESTED But that's just it—I think that part of our work
is *not* keeping to ourselves.

HEASLOP My dear, I know this country better than you. We
all come out here with the honest wish to do well, not
exactly mingle socially, but at least to close the gap a
little. One soon finds it only leads to trouble. India isn't
a drawing room. We're in India to do justice and keep
the peace. Them's my sentiments.

QUESTED (*quietly*) Your sentiments are those of a god.

HEASLOP (*trying to make amends*) India likes gods.

QUESTED And Englishmen like posing as gods.

HEASLOP Honestly, Adela, what do you want me to do?
Lose such power as I have for doing good in this country
because I don't slap Indians on the back?

QUESTED Of course not . . .

HEASLOP Well, it's what you're asking. You don't seem to
realize what my work involves—that the whole value
of my job depends on reputation for utter fairness. It's

the tradition of British justice. (*embarrassed*) It's not the kind of thing one goes *on* about, but I think it's a fine tradition.

QUESTED Oh, of course . . . so do I . . . but, Ronny, why can't you be pleasant to Indians?

HEASLOP Look, Adela, in any other country it would be different, but not in India. You'll soon find out that if I were to make friends with an Indian the gossip would be all over the bazaar in a minute. I'd be known as the kind of official an Indian can "get round". Don't you see how difficult and embarrassing it would be?

QUESTED But it has to begin *somewhere* . . .

HEASLOP If it were only my own discomfort I wouldn't mind so much, but really, I'd be undermining all the good we've tried to do in this wretched country——

QUESTED But I think we could do *more* good the other way . . .

HEASLOP Well, I haven't the choice. I'm too junior to dictate the manners of my fellow officials . . . or myself . . . even if I wanted to . . .

QUESTED Even if *I* wanted you to?

HEASLOP Adela, my dear, there is a lot I would do for you. But this is—I dare say I sound pompous—but *this is* a matter of principle. I can't help it if Indians don't like me . . . it's one of the hazards of the job. The thing I've learned out here—and you will too—is that we are better for them than they are for each other. Peace, security, good administration, justice . . . we've brought them all those.

QUESTED Everything except understanding.

HEASLOP What good will that do them?

QUESTED I don't know.

HEASLOP Well, there you are.

QUESTED (*with sudden passion*) But it's living in such isolation . . .

HEASLOP Isolation? When we have all our English friends. When we are surrounded by India and Indians?

QUESTED Exactly.

HEASLOP (*tolerantly*) Oh, I know you want to *understand* India, get to *know* the people and so on, but——

QUESTED (*rather desperately*) Somebody must!

HEASLOP Of course,

> *Smiling he continues with a change of tone, wanting to get the conversation on an affectionate level. She frowns and makes a small movement repudiating his tone. He quickly reverts to a more impersonal manner.*

and I've always approved of your doing good work here —as long as you don't get *involved* . . . social work, say —but please—Adela—please try not to be so emotional about it all.

QUESTED *Emotional?* . . . Ronny, we must have a thorough talk.

HEASLOP (*trying to avoid the implications of this*) I'm sorry. My temper's rotten in this heat. I don't mean to lecture you and order you about . . .

QUESTED I know——

HEASLOP But, of course, the way those Indians let you down this morning annoyed me, and things like that keep happening——

QUESTED It's nothing to do with them that I——

HEASLOP I dare say, but——

QUESTED It's something very different—it's that I think . . . I think we should . . . well, consider a bit more before we get married.

> *A long pause.*

HEASLOP (*sad but careful*) It's all right, Adela. No need to get upset. Take all the time you want. That was the arrangement you wanted . . . that we agreed on.

QUESTED (*with a rush of gratitude*) Oh, Ronny, I keep forgetting how nice you are—and I feel so ashamed of this —muddleheadedness. It's really not like me. I *could* explain—I need—breathing space.

HEASLOP (*uncomfortably*) No, really, Adela. You've acted entirely within your rights. I don't want you worrying and feeling guilty. So take your time, and don't fret. It will all work out, you'll see. You'll come round in the end.

QUESTED (*in a slightly despairing voice*) It's awful of me to have given you and your mother all this bother and still be so uncertain. (*a pause*) We've been very British over this, but I suppose that's all right.

HEASLOP (*smiling*) Since we *are* British, I suppose it is.

QUESTED Anyhow, we mustn't quarrel, Ronny.

HEASLOP Oh, I couldn't quarrel with you, Adela.

QUESTED I just need a little time——

HEASLOP Yes, yes. By all means . . . Time . . .

QUESTED Well—— (*she walks to the window and stands looking out at the garden*) Do you know the name of that green bird?

He comes to stand at her shoulder.

Up there, in the tree?

HEASLOP Bee-eater?

QUESTED Oh no, Ronny, it has red bars on its wings.

HEASLOP Parrot?

QUESTED (*laughs*) Good gracious no.

HEASLOP (*dejectedly*) McBryde has an illustrated book about birds. I'll borrow it for you if you like. I'm no good at all at birds. (*a pause*) In fact, I'm useless at anything outside the job of a City Magistrate. It's a great pity.

QUESTED (*turns to him suddenly and compassionately*) Oh, so am I, Ronny. I'm . . . useless at . . . everything. I'm really awful——

A pause while they stare at each other. Pleadingly.

HEASLOP Adela . . .

QUESTED (*sorry for him*) Ronny, I'd like to . . . tell you that I really will try to . . . work out the pattern of my life . . . here, with you.

38

HEASLOP (*making a move towards her which he quickly controls*) My darling . . . And I really will try to be more pleasant, if that is what you want——

QUESTED Well, at least to Dr. Aziz because he has been (*breaks off*) . . . he has been so kind to us. He has invited us to a picnic.

HEASLOP Us?

QUESTED Your mother, Mr. Fielding, Professor Godbole— exactly the same party.

HEASLOP Where on earth is this picnic to be?

QUESTED The Marabar Caves.

HEASLOP Well, I'm blessed. Did he descend to any details?

QUESTED (*getting heated*) If you had spoken to him, we could have arranged them.

> HEASLOP *shakes his head, laughing.*

Have I said anything funny?

HEASLOP I was only thinking how the worthy doctor's collar climbed up his neck.

QUESTED I thought we were discussing the caves.

HEASLOP So I am. Aziz was exquisitely dressed, from tie-pin to spats, but he had forgotten his back collar-stud, and there you have the Indian in a nutshell: inattention to detail; the fundamental slackness that reveals the race. Similarly to "meet" in the caves as if they were the clock at Charing Cross when they're miles from a station and each other.

QUESTED Have you been to them?

HEASLOP No, but I know all about them, naturally.

QUESTED Oh, naturally!

HEASLOP In any case, surely Fielding would never agree to an absurd scheme like that——

QUESTED And why not?

HEASLOP Well, he may not be quite our sort, but he has had *some* experience in this country . . .

> MRS. MOORE, FIELDING, AZIZ *and* GODBOLE *come in from the garden, sauntering along and talking*

39

pleasantly among themselves. HEASLOP *turns at once to* MRS. MOORE.

Mother! What is all this rubbish Adela has been telling me?

MOORE (*peaceably*)   I have no idea, my dear boy.

HEASLOP   I mean this nonsense about caves and picnics. Fielding, you are included, I hear—of course you will not allow such a fantastic scheme!

FIELDING   I don't presume to make decisions for other people, Heaslop.

HEASLOP (*looking from* MISS QUESTED *to* MRS. MOORE, *ignoring the Indians*)   If you are set on this ridiculous expedition then please allow me to arrange it. You can go under official auspices and that will be much better . . . and more comfortable too, without question.

> FIELDING *stands among the English, very embarrassed. He looks imploringly at* AZIZ.

QUESTED   But Dr. Aziz has already invited us to go with him.

HEASLOP   Very kind, I'm sure. But no doubt he will understand that you will be better off in our hands.

QUESTED   But that was the whole point—we wanted to go with the Indians—we could learn something.

HEASLOP (*shouting*)   Well, I consider the whole business foolish—yes, and dangerous!

MOORE (*quietly*)   Dangerous, Ronny?

HEASLOP (*furious*)   Yes, dangerous! In fact, Mother—Adela—I forbid it! I forbid you both! Of course I cannot speak for *Mr.* Fielding.

> FIELDING *makes a hopeless, awkward gesture towards* AZIZ. AZIZ *responds with the same Muslim salaam that established a rapport between them earlier. He smiles and quickly interrupts.*

AZIZ   I don't know whether you have all heard that Professor Godbole is a great authority on Indian music.

Indeed, he is much admired here in the College and elsewhere. What a great pity if you did not hear him. Professor, please do us the honour.

GODBOLE I will sing now.

> HEASLOP *takes an angry step forward and then stands still impatient and boiling.* MRS. MOORE *and* MISS QUESTED *turn towards* GODBOLE *listening politely.* GODBOLE *sings a brief Indian devotional song, while the English, with half their mind on their unresolved quarrel wait tensely. The* SERVANTS *appear on the edge of the verandah, the* MAN *at the waterchestnut tank stops work and straightens up. The Indians are enchanted. The English rigid and ill at ease.*

FIELDING Thanks so much. What was the song about?

MOORE Yes, do tell us.

GODBOLE I will explain in detail. It was a religious song. I place myself in the position of a milkmaiden. I say to Shri Krishna, "Come! Come to me only." The god refuses to come. I grow humble and say: "Do not come to me only. Multiply yourself into a hundred Krishnas, and let one go to each of my hundred companions, but one, O Lord of the Universe, come to me." He refuses to come. This is repeated several times. The song is composed in a raga appropriate to the present hour, which is the evening.

MOORE (*gently*) But he comes to you in some other song, I hope?

GODBOLE Oh no, he refuses to come. I say to him, "come, come, come, come, come, come." (*pause*) He neglects to come.

QUESTED Oh dear, that sounds so unsatisfactory!

HEASLOP (*interrupting*) Come along, Mother, Adela. We are already late for the polo. I am sure everyone will agree that you are not committed to this Marabar expedition.

MOORE I am committed to do nothing. Certainly not to

this polo. I find I am tired and prefer to rest. Will you drop me at the bungalow first?

QUESTED Drop me, too. I don't want to watch the polo either, I'm sure.

HEASLOP (*tired and disappointed*) Simpler to drop the polo. Well, come along, come along. (*he walks out angrily*)

MOORE Goodbye, Mr. Fielding, and thank you so much . . . . what lovely college grounds!

FIELDING Goodbye, Mrs. Moore.

QUESTED Goodbye. Such an interesting afternoon.

FIELDING Goodbye.

MOORE Goodbye, Dr. Aziz. We shall be seeing you soon again?

AZIZ May I hope so?

QUESTED (*earnestly making amends*) Oh, please, yes, Dr. Aziz. I don't know what to say . . .

AZIZ Say nothing, Miss Quested. You'll reconsider our picnic at the caves? I can fix the whole thing up in a jiffy. You'll see. That will be my great joy. To please you and Mr. Fielding.

QUESTED (*definitely*) I shall look forward to it. (*she looks uneasily from* AZIZ *to the path that* HEASLOP *took when he left*) Mrs. Moore! Dr. Aziz says that he is willing to arrange the picnic—what do you say?

MOORE I say I shall be delighted. Goodbye, goodbye.

> *They both nod to* GODBOLE, *who makes a namas-kar.* MISS QUESTED *responds to this. He follows them out to the garden, gently pointing out the way to the carriage.*

GODBOLE Goodbye—I will accompany the ladies.

FIELDING (*sinking exhausted into a chair*) Aziz, my dear chap. How am I to apologize to you?

AZIZ No apologies are necessary between friends.

FIELDING But you see, your other friends were right after all—oil and water.

AZIZ You will never persuade me of that. "The secret

understanding of the heart"—as I told you—I can't lose my faith in that for a moment's rudeness.

FIELDING I'm glad.

AZIZ I, too. Life is more interesting this way. I am only sorry for the embarrassment caused to your guests.

FIELDING Oh, they'll survive—they may even have accomplished what they set out to do—learn something about India.

AZIZ But still, it is unfortunate if your good ladies are caused distress.

FIELDING (*smiling at him affectionately*) You know what I should do, Aziz? I should get you a drink and then jog your elbow to make you spill it.

AZIZ (*puzzled for a moment*) I beg your pardon?

FIELDING (*sketching the gesture of a Muslim salaam and gently mimicking* AZIZ) "The sign of a generous heart, full to overflowing, you see."

AZIZ (*laughing*) You know, I invented that saying on the spur of the moment.

FIELDING You know (*putting his arm on* AZIZ's *shoulder, laughing with him*), I know you did.

> *They are both laughing with conspiratorial pleasure as the*

CURTAIN FALLS

ACT TWO. SCENE ONE

The scene a rocky hillside in the Marabar Hills, near the first of the Marabar Caves. On one side of the stage the opening of a cave can be partly seen. There is a small area of level ground near the centre of the stage, backed by jutting rocks. On the other side of the stage a narrow, uneven path winds upwards and off stage. On one side of the path the rocks rise sharply and with a formidable kind of beauty. On the other side of the path is indicated a sharp drop, not a precipice, exactly, but a very steep hill or gully. A few cactuses can be seen growing there, perhaps a stunted tree. When the curtain rises, FOUR SERVANTS *are seen scuttling on stage. They carry baskets and a number of white cloths. Behind them come a* FEW COOLIES *carrying deck chairs, a folding table, a cotton mat, a bundle of twigs tied together to make a broom, umbrellas, etc. With a good deal of shouting and indistinguishable orders, the servants set down their baskets, help the coolies to unload, unwind their turbans, wind them up again. One takes the broom and sweeps the level patch of ground, another spreads the mat over it. Others set up the table and chairs and ingeniously tie open umbrellas to the backs to provide shade. They unpack the baskets and are setting the table with crockery and silver when* DR. AZIZ *enters, followed by* MISS QUESTED, MRS. MOORE, GUIDE *and* SERVANT.

45

AZIZ Here we are! We arrive at last! At last we see the famous Marabar Caves! Mrs. Moore! Miss Quested! Is this not a magnificent sight? Welcome to Marabar!

QUESTED (*staring out to the precipice*) It looks as though we should have a wonderful view from over there.

AZIZ Yes, yes. First-rate view! . . . come, Mrs. Moore. Tell me, was the journey comfortable?

MOORE Oh yes!

AZIZ Are you tired?

MOORE Not a bit.

QUESTED Everything was very well arranged.

They stare off stage. AZIZ *points off into the distance.*

Well, I must say I can't see why Ronny made such a fuss . . . the only danger I can see is if one has no head for heights . . . In England there'd be a railing there.

AZIZ There is Chandrapore. Does it not look ridiculous from here? No more than a toy town.

MOORE But it is real . . . India is the only real country . . .

AZIZ Mrs. Moore, I knew that at heart you were an oriental . . .

QUESTED But what do you mean, the only real . . .

AZIZ It embraces everything, you see, Miss Quested.

MOORE Yes, I suppose that is what I mean. India knows the troubles of the whole world . . . but offers no promises, no solutions. It jumbles everything together, the ridiculous and the august . . . like life . . .

QUESTED Well, it certainly is an extraordinary landscape . . .

MOORE And you and I, Adela, are used to something more orderly. Something romantic yet manageable . . . there is no comfort here . . .

AZIZ (*who has not quite followed all this*) Comfort! Mrs. Moore you will be comfortable here, I promise you. Come and sit down in the shade and rest yourself . . .

As they return to the picnic site

Oh ladies, ladies. Put on your topis. Put on your topis,

46

the early sun is highly dangerous for heads. I speak as a doctor of course.

QUESTED (*laughing and imitating him*) And doctor, doctor, put on your own topi.

AZIZ (*laughing with her*) Not for my thick head. (*he takes her hand impulsively and bangs it on his head*) You see? Solid ivory!

> *She pulls her hand away rather suddenly but he doesn't notice. He fusses around* MRS. MOORE, *adjusting the umbrella, offering her a fan.*

QUESTED (*with a deep breath, taking a last look at the view*) I wouldn't have missed this for anything . . . (*standing at the picnic site*) How foolish of Mr. Fielding to have missed the train! When will he get another opportunity like this?

MOORE Never mind, he'll come on the next.

AZIZ But I am the host. I should have brought Mr. Fielding myself . . . and now . . . Mrs. Moore, Miss Quested, our expedition is a ruin.

MOORE (*smiling*) Mr. Fielding has no one to blame but himself. I see no ruin to our expedition.

AZIZ Really? Explain to me!

MOORE Now we shall all be Muslims together, as you promised.

AZIZ Oh my dear Mrs. Moore! You are perfect . . . What a great compliment . . . There is nothing I would not do for you! I would willingly die to make you happy!

MOORE (*laughing at his extravagance*) You make me giddy! (*more seriously*) I, too, wish for your happiness, Dr. Aziz.

AZIZ I should never have left Mr. Fielding in the care of Professor Godbole. A philosopher you see? So unreliable! Like those Calcutta people who never picked you up as planned and . . .

QUESTED (*uncomfortable*) Oh, that was a small incident . . .

47

nothing really . . . I should never have mentioned it. But you haven't told us about your own Calcutta trip . . .

AZIZ I postponed, I postponed. You see, I wanted to stay here and make foolproof arrangements for this picnic of ours.

QUESTED Oh dear, you changed your plans . . . just for us.

AZIZ No, no. For my own pleasure. I can visit my relative at any time at all. Only this morning I had a letter from him.

He pulls out his wallet and waves a letter to prove he is telling the truth and so to put them at their ease.

Poor man, he has a wife, a mother, five daughters . . . surrounded by women, you can see he's glad of a visit from me at any time at all.

QUESTED All the same, I do feel guilty . . .

AZIZ Never, never, Miss Quested! One of the greatest dreams of my life has been accomplished in having you two as my guests. I feel like the Emperor Babur.

QUESTED Babur? Why like him?

While he speaks, the SERVANTS *set out food.*

AZIZ Because my ancestors came down with him from Afghanistan. They joined him at Herat. He also had often no more elephants than one, none sometimes, but he never ceased showing hospitality.

QUESTED I thought another Emperor was your favourite . . . you mentioned him at Mr. Fielding's . . . what my book calls Aurangzebe.

AZIZ Aurangzebe, Alamgir? Oh yes, he was the more pious of the two. But Babur . . . his heart was filled with love.

QUESTED (*whispering*) *Love.*

AZIZ Oh yes . . . you know how he died? He laid down his life for his son. A death far more difficult than battle. They were caught in the heat, and at Agra his son fell sick. But Babur, he simply walked round the bed of his

48

son three times saying, "I have borne it away," and he did bear it away; the fever left his son and came to him, and he died. You see, love.

MOORE   Love in the heat.

She gives a deep sigh and MISS QUESTED *looks at her sharply.*

AZIZ   But I am keeping you from your food. I thought we would just have this little bit before the caves and breakfast afterwards.

He tells the SERVANTS *to offer food. They bring plates and stand behind* MISS QUESTED *and* MRS. MOORE.

QUESTED   Isn't this breakfast?

AZIZ   This breakfast? Do you think I would treat you so strangely?

QUESTED   It is all very well arranged.

AZIZ   That you will tell me only when we return to Chandrapore. Whatever disgraces I bring upon myself, you two remain as my guests. Your first outing is in my hands.

MOORE   But not necessarily our last. You know that we are to stay on here?

QUESTED (*after a pause*)   Yes.

AZIZ   Wonderful! Marvellous! I am so elated and flattered for my country! India has charmed you after all.

QUESTED (*flatly*)   I am to be married.

AZIZ   I know! I am glad it is happily settled!

QUESTED   To Mr. Heaslop.

AZIZ (*first taken aback*)   To Mr. Heaslop? Oh! This is a surprise! Well, never mind, never mind! (*bouncing about*) What excellent news! Many, many heartiest congratulations.

He springs up to shake her hands. She receives this with a rather furtive mixture of eagerness and reluctance.

Mrs. Moore, you must be so happy.

49

MOORE (*impatiently*) Yes, one has to see one's children settled. Then one is free oneself.

AZIZ And you, Miss Quested, you are certain to be happy with any relative of Mrs. Moore.

QUESTED Oh, my happiness . . . that's quite another problem. But, in any case, we shall stay here for some time longer. I for the major part of my life, I suppose. And Mrs. Moore, at least through the hot weather.

MOORE (*muttering*) Love in the heat . . .

AZIZ You will be married in Chandrapore? What an honour for our poor town.

QUESTED No, in the hills. But in future I intend to stay on the plains. I don't believe in the hot weather.

MOORE I believe in the hot weather, but I never thought it would bottle me up. They tell me I can't get away until after it's over.

QUESTED I won't be bottled up. I've no patience with these wives who leave their husbands every May. Mrs. McBryde hasn't stayed in the plains once since she married; she leaves her quite intelligent husband alone half the year and then is surprised she's out of touch with him.

MOORE She has children, you see. (*crossly*) Children are very demanding.

QUESTED Oh yes, that's true. Children.

AZIZ Children are the greatest joy. You must have many children.

QUESTED (*uneasily, looking away*) I'm not sure that I want any.

AZIZ (*irrepressibly*) Ah, children! Oh, Miss Quested (*he rushes to her*), since we are all being Muslims today, may I wish you, in the true Muslim way, a hundred sons?

QUESTED I'm . . . well I . . . Shouldn't we see the caves before the sun gets too high?

They all stand, MRS. MOORE *rather reluctantly.* THE GUIDE *appears and mutters to* AZIZ.

AZIZ   Quite right, quite right, Miss Quested. Walk ahead. Come, Mrs. Moore, the guide will lead you. The first cave is most conveniently placed just ahead of us. The guide tells me we must listen for the echo. Get inside and say something . . . anything. A word, a shout, and then listen for the remarkable echo. Walk on, walk on, I beg you.

> *The* GUIDE *leads the way to the partly visible entrance of the first cave, then stands back to let the ladies enter. He looks to* AZIZ *for guidance as to whether he should follow.* AZIZ *waves him on. Then feeling this is not enough of a performance for their first visit to the caves, he rounds up the* SERVANTS *and* COOLIES.

Go with them! Go with them! Go with my guests. Show them some honour . . .

> *He chivvies the whole group into the caves and follows them in. The stage is empty for a moment, and faintly a booming echo is heard, nothing comprehensible, but faintly ominous. It is repeated and swells and becomes confused.* MRS. MOORE *comes out first, looking shaken and ill. She goes directly to her chair and sits down. She fans herself and tips her head back, breathing heavily. A little later, the cave belches forth more humanity, and eventually* AZIZ *and* MISS QUESTED *come out too. She walks quickly to* MRS. MOORE.

QUESTED   Are you all right?

MOORE   . . . a bit stuffy in there . . . all those people in the dark.

QUESTED   Yes, a bit. You look pale. Do you feel ill?

MOORE *(sharply)*   No. Just a little tired, that's all. I'm not used to so much exertion so early in the day.

51

SALEM COLLEGE LIBRARY
WINSTON-SALEM, N. C.

QUESTED Oh, I see. Did you see when I struck the match? The reflection on the polished walls? Rather pretty, I thought.

MOORE . . . I . . . didn't notice.

QUESTED But Dr. Aziz says this wasn't the good cave, the best cave is around that path, there.

MOORE I don't think I am going on to the next cave. I do feel rather tired.

QUESTED You *aren't* well. We'll wait until after breakfast.

MOORE But that will disappoint him so. You go on. You don't mind, do you?

QUESTED No, of course not. He has been remarkably kind.

AZIZ (*coming up after a short colloquy with the* GUIDE) Well, Mrs. Moore. Miss Quested. What do you think? An extraordinary sight, don't you agree? Astonishing echo going round the cave.

QUESTED Quite fascinating.

AZIZ Come, we will try the next. This one, the guide tells me, is the most interesting. Wonderfully polished inside, like a mirror. Come, Mrs. Moore.

MOORE Dr. Aziz, forgive an old woman and let me stay here while you go on to the other cave. I find I am rather tired. I never was a very good walker.

AZIZ My dear Mrs. Moore, what does it matter as long as you are my guests? Indeed I am glad you are *not* coming, which sounds strange, but it means you are treating me with true frankness, like a friend.

MOORE (*seriously*) Yes, I am your friend . . . so may I make another suggestion? Don't have so many people with you this time. I think you'll find it . . . more convenient.

AZIZ Exactly, exactly. As you say. Nobody to accompany Miss Quested and myself, except the guide.

> AZIZ *and* MISS QUESTED *set out along the uneven path around the spur. The* GUIDE *leaps ahead of them, jumping from rock to rock in a manner that* MISS QUESTED *clearly can't imitate.*

QUESTED   Oh, my glasses!

> *She stops. She has forgotten her field-glasses.* AZIZ
> *notices her gesture and yells to a* SERVANT *to find*
> *them. While he is searching through hampers, the*
> *two stand talking.*

Tell me, Dr. Aziz, do you think it silly of me to give
in to Ronny . . . about being married in the hills.

AZIZ (*without much interest*)   No, no, very sensible. Much
cooler in the hills.

QUESTED   You were married in the hills?

AZIZ   For Indians it is different.

QUESTED   Your wife . . . what was she like?

AZIZ (*puzzled*)   She came from a good family. (*shrugs*) A
simple Muslim lady . . . a good wife . . .

QUESTED (*cautious, but compelled to ask*)   And you were
. . . happily married?

AZIZ   Oh very happily married. Although this will sound
strange to you, Miss Quested . . . although we had never
set eyes on each other until our wedding day.

QUESTED   It was all arranged by your families?

AZIZ   Yes, in the usual way. Very happily arranged.

QUESTED   And she never left you in the hot weather.

AZIZ (*laughing reminiscently with an overtone of past hap-*
piness)   Oh no. She never left me! I used to tease her
about it sometimes. She was—(*he sketches an evocative*
gesture as he talks) She wasn't exactly a Moghul princess, but she . . . well, no, she never left me.

QUESTED   How lucky. You must miss her terribly. Was
she your only wife?

AZIZ (*shocked and offended*)   Oh yes, one. One, in my own
particular case.

QUESTED (*she has caught his tone*)   But Muslims are allowed
four, are they not?

AZIZ (*staring at her*)   Man is . . . weak——

> *The* SERVANT *runs up with the field-glasses.* MISS
> QUESTED *puts the strap around her neck. She and*

53

AZIZ *set off on the path. They disappear from sight.*
MRS. MOORE *is leaning back in her deck chair, and
closes her eyes. The lights dim for a few seconds to
indicate the passage of time, and the booming
echo is heard again.*

. . . .

When the lights go up again, MRS. MOORE *is in
the same position, but the* COOLIES *and* SERVANTS
*have found themselves patches of shade and are
curled up asleep. A couple of the* SERVANTS *are
crouching nearby, talking in low voices. They are
facing away from the precipice. The sound has
awakened* MRS. MOORE. *She stirs and sits up
abruptly.*

MOORE (*not quite awake*) What happened? What was
that? Did something happen?

The SERVANTS *smile at her reassuringly, understanding the tone, though not the words.*

MOORE A dream . . . yes, a dream.

A pause, and then FIELDING *appears on the path.
He is mopping his face. He is followed after a
moment by* GODBOLE.

FIELDING Well, at last. Mrs. Moore, how are you?
MOORE So you've arrived at last, Mr. Fielding.
FIELDING Yes. Stupid of us to miss that train.
GODBOLE (*making a namaskar to* MRS. MOORE) It is my
fault. I am to blame. I made the delay.
FIELDING Oh, it doesn't matter, as long as we're here.
GODBOLE Alas, I was at my prayers when Mr. Fielding
so kindly came to my house. And time has no meaning
when one is praying.
FIELDING Well, never mind, never mind. Tell me, where
are Miss Quested and Dr. Aziz?
MOORE They went on to one of the further caves. I was
tired. I decided to stay here and rest.

54

FIELDING Probably very wise. From what I can gather, it is the view, more than the caves, that is impressive. (*a bit apprehensively*) Mrs. Moore, are you sure Miss Quested is with Dr. Aziz?

MOORE Oh yes.

FIELDING Then I must be mistaken. I thought I saw her clambering down the hillside as we came up the path.

MOORE (*harshly*) Which hillside?

FIELDING Well, I suppose it would be that one. You can see it from the place where the path curves round . . .

MOORE Why should she be climbing down hillsides?

FIELDING I can't imagine. Probably mistaken.

GODBOLE (*calmly*) Not mistaken. Possibly she dropped something and went in search of it.

FIELDING Then why not send a servant for it? (*thoughtfully*) Come to think of it, that gully is full of cactus . . . surely, she wouldn't . . .

MOORE So it begins like this . . .

FIELDING (*urgently*) Mrs. Moore, are you sure she was with Dr. Aziz?

MOORE (*indifferently*) Quite sure.

GODBOLE Pray be seated, Mr. Fielding. It is hot in the sun.

FIELDING If it really was Miss Quested, we could probably see her from here.

> *He runs up to the point where the path curves round the rock and looks over the gully. He shouts back to the others.*

There she is. She's reached the road below. She's just getting into a car.

> AZIZ *comes down the path and almost collides with* FIELDING.

AZIZ Fielding! My friend, you came! You joined at last. Now my day is complete.

FIELDING (*anxiously*) But what about Miss Quested? What is she doing down there?

AZIZ (*looks over. A pause*) But it is nothing at all. She came out of the caves, saw the car of her friend coming and decided on a ride back to town.

FIELDING But what friend? Who picked her up?

AZIZ How should I know? Doubtless she made some arrangement with a friend.

FIELDING It looked like Mrs. Callendar.

AZIZ Quite right. No doubt Mrs. Callendar came for her.

FIELDING (*partly reassured*) It seems a very odd way to behave.

AZIZ (*gaily*) Not a bit of it! Guests must be free to behave exactly as they wish. I should be hurt if they did otherwise.

FIELDING Well—I just hope she wasn't ill.

AZIZ Not a question of it. If she was ill she would have wanted me to attend her.

FIELDING (*at last reassured*) Yes, that makes sense.

GODBOLE Pray be seated, Mr. Fielding.

> AZIZ *following him sees the field-glasses near the rock. He stoops to pick them up, looks at them puzzled, and slips them in his pocket.*

AZIZ Professor Godbole, what a pleasure to see you! Sit down, sit down, all. We will have breakfast.

MOORE No breakfast for me, thank you.

FIELDING Godbole and I had breakfast at the station.

AZIZ Professor I am glad you came, for you, a scholar, can tell Mrs. Moore all the undoubtedly interesting history of the Marabar Caves.

GODBOLE I will tell Mrs. Moore the story of the Tank of the Dagger. Very interesting historical sight. Once there was a Hindu Raja who had slain his own sister's son. The dagger with which he performed this deed remained stuck to his hand until in the course of years he came to the Marabar Hills.

FIELDING Why did he come here? Is the place supposed to be sacred?

56

GODBOLE No, no. He came, and here he became thirsty and wanted to drink. But he saw here a thirsty cow and ordered water to be offered to her first. Which, when done, dagger fell from hand, and to commemorate miracle he built Tank.

MOORE (*after a pause*) I would have thought the miracle was the dagger sticking to the hand, rather than falling from it.

GODBOLE (*smiling*) Would you like to see the tank? It is quite near here.

AZIZ Are you rested enough, Mrs. Moore? Do not exert!

MOORE Yes, I think a short walk before we all go back to Chandrapore.

> *She and* GODBOLE *move in the direction of some rocks.*

GODBOLE If you're not too tired. It's just a little way up this hill.

MOORE No, no. I should like to go.

> (*They go out.*)

FIELDING Goodness, my dear fellow, what a trouble today has been for you!

AZIZ No trouble, no trouble.

FIELDING Guests not arriving on time, guests rushing away from the party. Tell me, Aziz, have you figured out what this picnic will cost you?

AZIZ Hush, my dear chap, don't mention the subject. Hundreds and hundreds of rupees. The completed account will be too awful. My friends' servants have robbed me right and left, and as for the elephant, she apparently eats nothing but gold.

FIELDING Monstrous!

AZIZ I am delighted, really. They have made my guests comfortable. If money goes, money comes. If money stays, death comes. Have you heard that proverb before? You couldn't, for I have just now invented it.

FIELDING Have you heard my proverbs? A penny saved is a penny earned; a stitch in time saves nine; look before you leap. And the whole British Empire rests on them. You will never kick us out, you know, until you make prudence a virtue here.

AZIZ Kick you out? Why should I worry about it? Leave it to the politicians . . . No, when I was a student I used to get excited over your damned countrymen, certainly; but now I think if I can be friends with one Englishman it is more important than being enemies with an entire nation. I don't really ask for more.

FIELDING As a friend, then—now don't be offended, Aziz —but as a friend, may I offer to share the expenses of this picnic with you?

AZIZ (*very touched*) No, no, my dear Fielding. The gesture is enough—the act would be too much.

> *Pause.* AZIZ *takes a cheap little cardboard folder from his pocket and hands it to* FIELDING.

Open it.

FIELDING (*opens it and pulls out a photograph.*) Who is it?

AZIZ She was my wife. You are the first Englishman she has ever come before. Now put her photograph away.

FIELDING (*too dazed to do so*) I don't think I have ever been so deeply complimented and I can't imagine why——

AZIZ It's nothing. She was not a highly educated lady. She was not even beautiful. She was my wife. Put her away. She is dead. She is of no importance. I showed her to you because I have nothing else to show.

> FIELDING *returns the photograph.*

Miss Quested was asking about my marriage just now and that is why she is so much on my mind.

FIELDING Miss Quested, all facts and curiosity. She wants to know *about* India, not really to know India.

AZIZ Yes, I'm glad you're not going to marry her.

FIELDING I? Marry her? What on earth put that extra-ordinary idea into your head?

AZIZ I don't know—something you said—and I wished marriage and children for you.

FIELDING Good Lord! Not with her, she's going to marry Heaslop.

AZIZ Yes, I'm glad it's not with her for she is not even beautiful. She has practically no breasts if you come to think of it. For the City Magistrate they shall be sufficient perhaps, but for you I shall arrange ... (*he is back to his old grandiloquent style*) I shall arrange a lady with breasts like ...

FIELDING I know, like pomegranates ... (*laughing*)

AZIZ (*also laughing*) I was going to say mangoes ...

FIELDING In any case, you'll do no such thing.

AZIZ Not really. Only a gesture to match your gesture ...

> *He sketches the gesture of a Muslim salaam as he did in the first act and* FIELDING *responds as before. During this speech* MRS. MOORE *and* GODBOLE *return slowly to the picnic site.* FIELDING *sees them and is again nagged with worry.*

FIELDING You know, I still can't help feeling that something went wrong here ... it seems such an extraordinary way for a girl like Miss Quested to behave.

AZIZ (*springing up*) Mrs. Moore, I appeal to you ... did anything go wrong with my arrangements? Are you dissatisfied with me?

MOORE On the contrary, your arrangements were perfect. Nothing went wrong.

AZIZ You see, Fielding? You see?

FIELDING But something must have happened ...

MOORE (*crossly*) Forgive me, Dr. Aziz, I know I am being a very awkward guest, but unless you particularly want to stay longer, could we not go back to Chandrapore?

AZIZ Of course, of course, anything you wish. We have seen all, we have had our little excursion. Now back to our homes and rest, rest, rest!

He starts to chivvy the SERVANTS *again. They jump up and bustle about folding chairs and clearing up. He mutters more orders.* GODBOLE *goes out.*

FIELDING (*thoughtfully*) So nothing happened...

MOORE (*very sharply*) Of course something happened, Mr. Fielding.

FIELDING Did it? Then...

MOORE (*impatient*) But it is too late now. She has started the machine; it must run to its end. The machine (*she taps her head*) to kill love.

She goes out. The SERVANTS *are still flapping about.*

AZIZ (*to* FIELDING, *smiling*) Come, my dear Fielding. You have seen Marabar at last. That is something.

FIELDING Aziz... I'm really worried...

AZIZ Leave the worrying to me, my dear fellow.

FIELDING But did you hear what Mrs. Moore said?

AZIZ She is old... and tired. Probably she will soon forget this day. (*joyfully*) But I—I shall remember this day forever. Come.

They leave together as the

CURTAIN FALLS

ACT TWO. SCENE TWO

The scene is the English Club of Chandrapore. It is late afternoon of the day of the picnic at the Marabar Caves. The Club smoking-room has been arranged for a meeting, a table on one side to serve as an informal podium, rows of rattan chairs facing the table. The tall shuttered doors of the smoking-room open on to a verandah, and beyond the verandah railing, in the blue distance, the irregular, implacable outline of the Marabar Hills can be seen. On one side swing doors lead into the Club bar. On the other, closed doors shut off the lounge. When the Curtain goes up there is a certain amount of indistinct talk from the bar where the men are having drinks and discussing in serious voices the affair at the caves. At intervals one or another of the men leans through the bar door to see that the women are all right, to murmur a reassuring word or two, to see whether Mr. Turton, the Collector (Chief Administrative Officer for the district), has arrived. Sitting in the smoking-room, with anxious important looks on their faces, are the various wives. MRS. TURTON *is, of course, the centre of the group and when one of the men looks at her enquiringly to get news of Mr. Turton's whereabouts and plans, she shakes her head soberly. All the ladies, one by one, look up significantly at the closed lounge doors with impatient and worried expressions. It is clear from their behaviour that something alarming is going on behind those doors.*

There is a sudden clatter of temple bells and drums that makes the ladies sit up nervously, alert and apprehensive. One of the men from the bar puts his head out to reassure them. He is a Lieutenant in the khaki tropical uniform of an Indian Army Regiment.

MRS. TURTON   Well, Mrs. Collin, we must come to some decision about the price of these tickets. I suggest three rows at ten rupees . . .

MRS. MCBRYDE   Don't you realize that you're wasting your time with this sort of thing when there's likely to be a riot?

MRS. TURTON   This is not the time for hysterical outbursts. The best thing we can do is to get on with our own work.

MRS. LESLEY   Mrs. Turton, how can you worry about such things, when that poor girl is lying in there . . .

MRS. TURTON   Mrs. Lesley, there is nothing we can do.

MRS. LESLEY   But after that terrifying attack in a cave . . .

MRS. TURTON   Mr. McBryde and Mr. Heaslop are in there with her now. Now, Mrs. Collin, to continue . . .

LIEUTENANT *enters.*

LIEUTENANT   No cause for alarm, ladies. We have people posted in the city . . .

MRS. MCBRYDE   But what is it? Is it a demonstration?

LIEUTENANT   No, no. Just preparations for some festival.

MRS. MCBRYDE   The story is bound to be all over the bazaars by now.

LIEUTENANT   Nothing to worry about. We are very well protected, I assure you. (*He returns to the bar.*)

MRS. TURTON   I'm sure the lieutenant is right. We will only aggravate things by seeming anxious . . . It seems unkind to say it now but I knew it would end badly. All these foolish attempts to *see* India . . .

MRS. BURTON   But who could know it would end as badly as this?

MRS. LESLEY   The whole idea of a picnic at Marabar . . . no one but a novice would think of such a thing—I mean with *Indians*!

MRS. MCBRYDE (*in a high, tense voice*)   That's just what I mean . . . the Indians. How can we stay calm when we never know which of them . . .

MRS. TURTON   Please . . .

MRS. MCBRYDE   I can't help it. I have children . . .

MRS. LESLEY (*with an air of stating a self-evident truth*)   I always think the children should be educated at home. I mean, what with the climate . . .

MRS. MCBRYDE (*with rising resentment*)   People are always saying things like that—but what about *us*? Are *we* always to have only half a life—*always* separated from either husband or children?

MRS. TURTON (*almost off-hand*)   One of the penalties of responsibility. It has its compensations too.

MRS. MCBRYDE (*angrily*)   But I tell you——

MRS. TURTON   Mrs. McBryde, I can't allow this. From you of all people. Your husband's here now in charge. We look to him to protect us, and you must . . .

MRS. MCBRYDE   Protect you with what? Native policemen? Native troops? It's ridiculous . . .

MRS. TURTON (*very emphatically*)   This . . . must . . . stop! Now, control yourself. We mustn't jump to conclusions. It is just possible there may be some other explanation.

MRS. COLLIN   You're quite right, Mrs. Turton. When you've been here as long as I have . . .

MRS. MCBRYDE   What are the other possible explanations? . . .

MRS. LESLEY   The poor girl may be dying . . .

MRS. TURTON   The doctor is with her now, we won't improve things by arguing like this.

The other ladies are openly sceptical and murmur things like "You're too charitable, Mrs. Turton," and "Well, I suppose we must keep open minds . . ."

MRS. MCBRYDE   I'm not going to put up with it . . . I'm not! I'm going to leave.

MRS. BURTON   Leave India?

MRS. MCBRYDE   I'll make my husband resign, and yes, we'll leave India and return . . .

MRS. BURTON   To what?

MRS. MCBRYDE   To what? To England, of course.

They all know this is impossible since none of them could maintain their colonial living standards in England.

MRS. BURTON   Things aren't the same for us . . . things aren't so easy in England . . .

MRS. MCBRYDE   But at least . . . Well, we can ask for a transfer, that would be something . . .

Behind her back the ladies exchange looks, and then continue in silence their small occupations . . . one knits, another flips through the pages of an old copy of the "Illustrated London News," and so on. HEASLOP *comes in from the lounge and the ladies are all alert again, watching him.*

HEASLOP   Callendar has given her a light sedative . . . She's in a bad . . . a very bad way . . .

MRS. TURTON   Will she talk to him?

HEASLOP   Oh, she talks. She talks all the time . . . too much . . .

MRS. BURTON   You mean, she's, well . . . she's *raving*?

MRS. COLLIN   More likely delirious.

HEASLOP   Well, the sedative should calm her a bit. She has a high temperature. And Callendar is worried about the cactus thorns . . .

MRS. TURTON   *Cactus* . . . oh, the poor creature . . .

HEASLOP   In case they infect... Anyway she is ready to make a statement now. I mean an official police statement.

MRS. BURTON   Then she's...

MRS. MCBRYDE   Then it really is...

HEASLOP   Yes, it really is just as bad as we feared.

FLETCHER *comes in.*

FLETCHER   The Collector Sahib just phoned to say he's on his way up. Arrangements seem to be pretty complete in the city. Would you tell Callendar and McBryde please.

HEASLOP   Thank you, Mr. Fletcher.

FLETCHER *looks searchingly at* HEASLOP, *then ducks into the bar and* RONNY *returns to the lounge.*

MRS. MCBRYDE   (*in a low fierce voice*)   I knew it... I told you...

MRS. TURTON   Well, we've all known it really. Why else would our husbands have started on security arrangements immediately. But these things have to be confirmed. After all, we do not have a reputation for fairness for nothing.

MRS. BURTON   I entirely agree, Mrs. Turton. But now we know for sure.

MRS. MCBRYDE   I knew for sure all the time... I did! That ... that monster ...

MRS. LESLEY   Really!

MRS. TURTON   Well, he'll be punished, make no mistake.

MRS. MCBRYDE   Punished after the damage is done ...

MRS. BURTON   He could hardly be punished *before* ...

MRS. TURTON   (*severely*)   The situation should never have arisen. Never. But the poor girl... in spite of her foolishness ...

A certain bustle outside announces the arrival of MRS. MOORE *and* FIELDING. *She is uninterested, even expressionless. He is puzzled, anxious, energetic. The ladies surround* MRS. MOORE *at the verandah*

65

door, and MRS. TURTON *makes a point of shaking hands with her.*

ALL   Oh, Mrs. Moore.

MRS. TURTON   Thank God you got here safely, Mrs. Moore. What a terrible day!

A WIFE   Mrs. Moore, are you all right? Do come in——

FIELDING   What *is* all this about? Ladies . . . please? We are mystified . . .

MRS. TURTON (*nastily*)   We thought *you* would be able to tell *us*, Mr. Fielding.

FIELDING   Tell you what? Is there to be a meeting here? We were instructed most urgently to come directly here from the station.

MRS. TURTON (*ominously*)   Indeed there is to be a meeting.

FIELDING   But what has happened? We have been at the Marabar Caves all day and know nothing.

MRS. COLLIN   Exactly, Mr. Fielding.

MRS. TURTON   You have been on the very spot and were helpless to prevent this horrible thing. What has happened indeed!

FIELDING   A riot? Disturbance of some kind? There seemed to be a lot of police on the road, but I assumed that was because of the Mohorrum celebrations.

MRS. TURTON   You, of course, know the names of all these native festivals.

MRS. MOORE   I dare say it is about Adela.

FIELDING   Adela? Miss Quested?

MRS. MOORE   She has been unwell lately.

MRS. TURTON   You see, Mr. Fielding, Mrs. Moore appears to know all about it. It is strange that you should pretend ignorance.

FIELDING   Unwell? Sick? Since when? (*ignoring* MRS. TURTON).

MRS. MOORE   Oh, a few days . . . anyway since before this excursion to the caves.

MRS. TURTON (*startled*)   Since before . . .

FIELDING   Didn't we decide she was all right...

MRS. MOORE (*impatiently*)   Not physical illness.

FIELDING   I'm not sure that I understand.

MRS. MOORE (*in exasperation*)   I suppose, since you insist, one must call it a spiritual illness.

FIELDING   Mrs. Moore, you trouble me very much.

MRS. MOORE   Oh, trouble, trouble! Muddles and mysteries! Let me pass, Mr. Fielding. I'm tired and I wish to sit down.

> *She finds a chair separated from the rest and remains there for the rest of the act, a disapproving, compelling figure. She says very little, but nobody can ignore her or her occasional movements of irritation or weariness.*

LADIES   Poor creature...
  I think she's a little unhinged...
  After today, who could wonder?

> MAJOR CALLENDAR *enters from the lounge. He looks crumpled and hot, but retains his bluff manner.*

CALLENDAR   Well, ladies...

MRS. TURTON (*calling out to the men in the bar*)   Major Callendar has come out.

> *They come out of the bar with drinks in their hands. The* LIEUTENANT, MR. BURTON, *a* CIVIL SERVANT, *a* FEW JUNIORS *from the various civil departments.*

MEN   Well, Doctor Sahib?
  How is she? Is she all right?
  Good to see you, Callendar...
  Let's hope you can set our minds at rest...

BURTON   Squat down, Callendar, and tell us all about it.

CALLENDAR   Take me some time to do that.

BURTON   Have a drink. (*he gets it*) Is she worse? She was in a terrible state when she arrived.

CALLENDAR (*accepting a drink*) Not worse. She is by no means out of danger.

MRS. TURTON Any one of us would be glad to sit with her ... or anything ...

CALLENDAR Most generous of you, Mrs. Turton, but it isn't necessary. My wife will stay with her ... she's had experience. (*there is a short difficult pause*) I've never had such a case in all my life ... and had never hoped to, particularly here, in India. (*he shakes his head*) Fever, of course. Only to be expected. And the cactus thorns. Those will have to be removed under a magnifying glass. One by one. They are all over her. (*he takes a long drink*) But what am I to do about the rest of it? Her mind ... the disturbance in her mind. And the terrors ... it's more than ... well, we'll just have to wait and see. (*he shrugs and then turns hopefully to* MRS. MOORE) Mrs. Moore, perhaps you can help me. Miss Quested complains of what she calls "an echo". Inside her head, she says. As though her head were a cave. An echo.

MRS. MOORE (*indifferently*) Yes. There was one.

CALLENDAR (*gently*) Was it something to do with the cave?

MRS. MOORE Oh yes. But there was nothing distinctive about the echo in the cave.

CALLENDAR I'm sorry to press this, but if you could help me ... explain it to me a bit, I might be able to do something for her.

MRS. MOORE (*in a monotone*) "Boum"—or something like that. Whatever is said, the same monotonous noise replies. "Boum" is the sound as far as I can express it, or "bou-oum," or "ou-boum" ... utterly dull. Hope, politeness, the blowing of a nose, the squeak of a boot, all produce "Boum".

> *Baffled silence while they all exchange looks and someone taps his head suggestively.*

CALLENDAR (*stands up restlessly*) I can't help blaming myself . . . I wish I hadn't given my *jewel* of an assistant leave . . . It would never have happened . . .

FLETCHER Rubbish—you couldn't have been expected to foresee.

FIELDING Assistant? Do you mean Aziz?

MEN No one blames you, Callendar.
We are all to blame. (*they look meaningly at* FIELDING)
We assumed that as long as there was an Englishman along with the party . . .

FIELDING (*pushing forward*) But what about Dr. Aziz? How is he involved?

CALLENDAR (*shocked*) Fielding, can you seriously insist that you don't know?

FIELDING (*patiently*) We were brought straight here from the station when we returned from the picnic. We have since learned that Miss Quested is ill. Dr. Aziz was taken off somewhere at the same time. That is all I know.

CALLENDAR Somewhere! To the police station . . . where he belongs. The Collector was kind enough to save you from the disgrace of being seen with him . . .

FIELDING I am grateful to Mr. Turton, for his kindness. But what has Aziz done?

> TURTON *enters and stands in the door unseen by the others.*

CALLENDAR (*slowly and with distaste*) Miss Quested was attacked and insulted in one of the Marabar Caves.

FIELDING What?

CALLENDAR She escaped, by God's grace.

FIELDING Oh no . . . not Aziz . . . it couldn't be Aziz . . .

> CALLENDAR *nods.* FIELDING *pulls himself together.*

Who brings this . . . this wicked charge?

CALLENDAR My wife, and the unfortunate girl herself.

FIELDING Miss Quested? Miss Quested, *herself* definitely accuses him . . .

CALLENDAR (*coldly*) Yes.

FIELDING ... of attempted rape?

CALLENDAR Yes.

FIELDING (*violently*) Then she's mad.

> MR. TURTON, *the Collector, has stood in the verandah door listening, now moves forward, rigid with fury. The others deferentially make way for him, and group themselves like students listening to a respected teacher.*

TURTON I cannot pass that remark. As Collector of this district I must ask you to withdraw it instantly. It is the type of remark you have permitted yourself to make ever since you came to Chandrapore.

FIELDING I am excessively sorry, sir; I certainly withdraw it unconditionally.

TURTON Mr. Fielding, what induced you to speak in such a tone.

FIELDING The news gave me a very great shock, so I must ask you to forgive me. I cannot believe that Dr. Aziz is guilty.

TURTON (*slams his hand on the table*) That...this is a repetition of your insult in an aggravated form.

FIELDING If I may venture to say so, no. I make no reflection on the good faith of the two ladies, but the charge they are bringing against Aziz rests upon some mistake, and five minutes will clear it up.

TURTON (*biting and vindictive*) It does indeed rest upon a mistake. It does indeed. I have had twenty-five years' experience of this country. And during that time I have never known anything but disaster result when English people and Indians attempt to be intimate socially. We must meet them, yes. Courtesy, by all means. Intimacy ...never. The whole weight of my experience is against it. You, Mr. Fielding, with your "liberal" ideas, you want peace and sound administration, a comfortable life and time to get on with your work...believe me, *we* are the ones that make that possible for you. And gladly. But you demand more. You demand that everyone be treated on equal terms ... in an instant you see what happens. The work of years is undone and the good name of my District, which means a great deal to me, is ruined for a generation.

FIELDING   I ask only that one man ... one Indian be considered a human being.

TURTON   And I am talking of a large community, Mr. Fielding. Both—Britons and Indians. Perhaps you can see the end of this day's work. I only wish that I had never lived to see its beginning. That a young lady— engaged to my most valued subordinate ... that an English girl fresh from home ... that she should have been led ... by ...

> *His accusation of* FIELDING *is obvious, and so are the signs of his sincere distress. The club members register a kind of approval of both. After a moment he straightens up, looks around at them all, and continues his speech to* FIELDING *in a more controlled voice.*

Well, once again, it is left to us to clear up the mess when newcomers set our traditions aside.

FIELDING   We all know that you are referring to me, sir ...

TURTON   Mr. Fielding, did it not occur to you to wonder why Miss Quested did not return with the rest of your party on the train?

FIELDING   But I thought I knew why. I saw her leave ... (*turning helplessly to the others*) As you probably know, Professor Godbole and I were delayed and missed the early train ...

BURTON (*meaningly*) Delayed?

FIELDING   I was to pick Godbole up on my way to the station. When I got to his house he was saying his prayers and could not be disturbed.

Someone laughs. Someone says, "Oh, it's called a delay, now, is it?" Someone else says, "Prayers! We all know those prayers!"

FLETCHER Look, Fielding, we have reason to believe that Godbole was bribed.

FIELDING Bribed by Aziz? What on earth for?

FLETCHER To hold you up—delay you, if you prefer. It was all premeditated, you see.

FIELDING I don't see. I only know that when Godbole and I got there I saw her from the top of the hill. A car had stopped there and I saw someone—a woman—get out and help her in. I thought that Miss Quested had seen the chance of a lift back to Chandrapore and had very sensibly taken it instead of the hot train ride. Perhaps she recognized the car and hailed it.

Silence.

It's possible. (*getting a bit desperate*) Callendar—I couldn't really tell from the distance, but it looked as though it might be your wife? She could confirm it?

CALLENDAR It was my wife all right. And we can all count ourselves extremely fortunate that she happened to be passing Marabar at just that moment. She drove the poor girl straight back here.

MRS. TURTON Yes. Thank God she was passing. I cannot think of what might have happened otherwise.

FIELDING (*seeing no help from them*) Mrs. Moore. You were there. What happened? Was Miss Quested in a hurry to get home—and grabbed at this unexpected opportunity?

MRS. MOORE Adela? She's never been in a hurry in her life.

FIELDING If she wasn't feeling well, and didn't want to bother the rest of the party? A touch of the sun, perhaps?

MOORE (*vaguely*) I wasn't feeling very well myself.

FIELDING So it could have been the sun?

MOORE Not the sun. I went into the first cave with them. It seemed as if a lot of people crushed in after us . . .

72

the closeness of those people ... and the crush ... and the smell ... and, of course the echo ... I was suffocated. I didn't go to the next cave with them. I wasn't feeling very well.

CALLENDAR Well, there you are, Fielding. He bribed Godbole to delay, and he must have bribed the servants and guides to stifle Mrs. Moore. What more do you want? It's perfectly clear ...

MOORE It was the echo ...

CALLENDAR I call it very neatly planned. Mrs. Moore out of commission. Aziz is free to go on with the girl to the next cave. Alone. And then ... well, better give up trying to find excuses, Fielding.

    FIELDING *turns away defeated.*

TURTON That's enough now. I think we have made the position clear to Mr. Fielding.

    Enter MCBRYDE *who stands beside* TURTON.

CALLENDAR Ah, McBryde—How is she?

TURTON Ah, McBryde, that was very quick. Now we have some first hand official information?

MCBRYDE Yes sir, we have more than information. We have evidence. I wish I could feel some satisfaction about it all.

TURTON We are all shocked and distressed, McBryde. But if you have evidence, then that is at least something concrete on which to base our actions.

MCBRYDE Yes sir. It's concrete all right. I'm afraid the case will definitely have to come to trial now. There seems no doubt about it. (*producing some notes*) Well, sir, I have taken down the poor girl's initial charge signed and witnessed. (*he shows the papers to* TURTON) I couldn't worry her overmuch with questions. She's in no state ... and besides, she'll have plenty to go through in the witness-box.

FIELDING Wasn't there a guide with her? Aziz said there would be guides ...

MCBRYDE   Guide? No. She had got among some cactuses. Mrs. Callendar saved her life coming just then . . . the girl was beginning to fling herself about. Mrs. Callendar helped her down to the car. Miss Quested couldn't stand the native driver and kept saying "Keep him away" . . . and it was that that put Mrs. Callendar on the track of what had happened. That's the story so far as I know it. Perhaps later Miss Quested will be able to tell us more, but certainly not just now. There was an echo that appears to have frightened her.

FIELDING   Exactly. The echo . . . couldn't that have been . . . ?

MRS. TURTON   But Mrs. Moore tells us that it wasn't a frightening echo. Just a sort of "boum".

MRS. MOORE   You are wrong. It was both frightening and disagreeable. Worse than the crush of people and the smells and the suffocation. It undermined one's hold on life. It said, "Pathos, piety, courage . . . they exist, but are identical, and so is filth. Everything exists, nothing has value." If one had spoken vileness in that place or quoted poetry, the comment would have been the same —"ou-boum". If one had spoken with the tongues of angels and pleaded for all the unhappiness and mis-understanding in the world, past, present and to come, for all the misery men must undergo whatever their opinion and position, and however much they dodge or bluff . . . it would amount to the same.

Another bewildered silence.

FIELDING   So there is still room for error. Is it possible that this echo affected Miss Quested's nerves? That she has confused events in her own mind?

MCBRYDE (*sadly*)   Oh no. She is very clear about that. It was when she went to the second cave. The charge is that he followed her into the cave and made insulting advances. She hit at him with her field-glasses; he pulled

74

at them and the strap broke, and that is how she got away.

FIELDING   No, no. There must . . .

MCBRYDE   When we searched him at the Police Station, they were in his pocket.

FIELDING   Oh no, oh no, no; it'll be cleared up in five minutes . . .

MCBRYDE (*placing them on the table, unemotionally*)   Have a look at them. The strap has been newly broken. The eye-piece is jammed . . . What does the logic of evidence say?

FIELDING *shakes his head.*

MCBRYDE   We have further evidence of his character and his state of mind. (*he puts* AZIZ's *wallet on the table*) Look at this, for instance. We took it from him at the same time. I have been going through the contents. They are not edifying. Here is a letter from a friend who keeps a brothel in Calcutta!

FIELDING (*sickened*)   . . . his private letters . . .

MCBRYDE   It'll have to be quoted in court as bearing on his morals. He was arranging to visit this man and see women. It's clear what thoughts filled his head. And we found more evidence on him, too. Look at this. You see, photographs of women.

FIELDING (*examines photograph*)   That's his wife.

TURTON   How do you know that?

FIELDING   He told me. It was a great compliment for a Muslim to show me the picture of his wife.

CALLENDAR   Wife, indeed! We all know those wives.

TURTON   Well, whatever our thoughts may be, there is certainly no question that McBryde has produced all the relevant evidence necessary for this case. We all know how quickly gossip spreads in the bazaar, and how fast things become exaggerated. Consequently it is our job to keep from panic and alarmism which is as dangerous for us as it is for the entire city. Certainly we may expect tense days ahead, but we must keep cool. No matter what happens. No inflammatory talk. No open anxiety. Keep cool. Don't go out more than you can help. Don't go into the city. Don't talk before your servants. Meanwhile I'd prefer if you would all remain here until I have had a talk with Heaslop. Right? My dear . . .

> TURTON *goes out. The meeting breaks up and people separate into groups, some return to the bar, some to the verandah. Only* MRS. MOORE *remains sitting exactly as before.* FIELDING *stops* MCBRYDE *as he is leaving.*

FIELDING McBryde, forgive me a moment. May I have a word with you? I suppose there is no possibility of my seeing Miss Quested?

MCBRYDE I hardly think that would do. Surely.

FIELDING I was afraid you'd say that. I should very much like to.

MCBRYDE She is in no state to see anyone. Besides, you don't know her well.

FIELDING Hardly at all . . . But you see I believe that that wretched boy is innocent and she's under some hideous delusion.

MCBRYDE I had no idea that *that* could be in your mind.

FIELDING Those field-glasses upset me for a moment, but I've thought since; it's impossible that, having attempted to assault her, he would put her glasses into his pocket.

MCBRYDE Quite possible, I'm afraid. When an Indian goes bad he goes not only very bad but very odd.

FIELDING I don't follow you.

> *The two sit down.*

MCBRYDE How should you? When you think of crime you think of English crime. The psychology here is different. I dare say you'll tell me next that he was quite normal when he came down the hill to greet you . . . Which must have been immediately after the attack.

76

FIELDING   He was. And he was normal and cheerful and hospitable all the rest of the day too.

MCBRYDE   No reason why he shouldn't be. I've seen it again and again. Read any of the Mutiny records.

FIELDING   However that may be, I do want to see Miss Quested.

MCBRYDE   You haven't explained to me what's in your mind. Why on earth do you want to see her?

FIELDING   I only wanted to ask her whether she is certain, dead certain, that it was Aziz who followed her into the cave.

MCBRYDE   Possibly I might ask her that much.

FIELDING   But *I* wanted to ask her. I wanted someone who believes in him to ask her.

MCBRYDE   What difference does that make?

FIELDING   She is among people who disbelieve in Indians.

MCBRYDE   She tells her own story, doesn't she?

FIELDING   I know, but she tells it to *you*.

MCBRYDE   Well, whatever your finespun theories may be, you can't see her.

FIELDING   (*angrily*) I can see your prisoner, I suppose?

MCBRYDE   His own people seem in touch with him all right. Why should you mix yourself up with pitch?

FIELDING   But if he's innocent . . .

MCBRYDE   Innocent or guilty, why mix yourself up? What's the good?

FIELDING   Oh good, good! I feel suffocated.

MCBRYDE   Look, Fielding, the situation is going to be very nasty in Chandrapore and we shall all have to hang together I'm afraid. At a time like this there's no room for . . . well . . . personal views. The man who doesn't toe the line is lost.

FIELDING   (*bitterly*) I can see that.

MCBRYDE   But you don't see entirely. He not only loses himself, he weakens his friends. If you leave the line, you leave a gap in the line. These jackals who call themselves his lawyers are looking with all their eyes for a

77

gap. Besides, the results could be very serious for you
...for your career.

FIELDING   Can I see Aziz?

MCBRYDE   No. You may see him on a magistrate's order,
but on my own responsibility I don't feel justified. It
might lead to more complications.

FIELDING (*icily*)   To whom do I apply for an order?

MCBRYDE   City Magistrate.

FIELDING   Heaslop! That sounds very comfortable!

MCBRYDE   Yes, one can't very well worry poor Heaslop.

> *Through the last few speeches there has been a
> good deal of quiet movement and whispering that
> spreads from the verandah to the bar. People start
> returning to the smoking-room. The groups that
> stayed in the room sit up alertly.* HEASLOP *enters.
> Everyone except* FIELDING *stands up.*

HEASLOP   Oh please—please everyone sit down. I only
wanted to hear what has been decided.

TURTON (*his hand on* HEASLOP's *shoulder*)   Heaslop, I was
telling them earlier that I'm against any show of force.
I'm afraid it would prove only an invitation to more
trouble, even violence and rebelliousness. (*apologetically*)
When the verdict is obtained, it will be another matter.

HEASLOP   You are sure to know best; I have no experience...

MRS. TURTON   How is Miss Quested, may we ask?

HEASLOP   Quieter, thank you. I wish everyone would sit
down.

CALLENDAR   Some have never got up.

> *They all stare at* FIELDING. FIELDING *remains
> seated.*

TURTON   Mr. Fielding, what has prevented you from standing up?

FIELDING   May I make a statement, sir?

TURTON   Certainly.

78

FIELDING I believe Dr. Aziz to be innocent.

TURTON You have a right to hold that opinion if you choose, but is that any reason why you should insult Mr. Heaslop?

FIELDING May I conclude my statement?

TURTON Certainly.

FIELDING I am waiting for the verdict of the courts. If he is guilty I resign from my service and leave India. I resign from the Club now.

TURTON You have not answered my question. Why did you not stand when Mr. Heaslop entered?

FIELDING (*moving towards the door*) With all deference, sir, I am not here to answer questions, but to make a personal statement, and I have concluded it.

TURTON (*furious*) May I ask whether you have taken over charge of this District? (*as* FIELDING *reaches the door and finds the* LIEUTENANT *blocking the way*) One moment, Mr. Fielding, you are not to go yet, please. Before you leave the Club from which you do very well to resign, you will express some detestation of the crime, and you will apologize to Mr. Heaslop.

FIELDING I shall wait to hear whether, in fact, there was a crime before I decide whether I should apologize to all of you or to Dr. Aziz.

TURTON (*losing control*) Leave this room at once! I deeply regret that I demeaned myself to have you met at the station. You have sunk to the level of your associates, that is what is wrong with you! Leave this room at once ...

FIELDING I cannot while this gentleman prevents me.

HEASLOP (*almost in tears*) Let him go! For God's sake, let him go!

> *The* LIEUTENANT *moves away from the door and* FIELDING *exits.*

TURTON (*a pause while he pats* HEASLOP *on the back*) My

dear Heaslop, I'm sure I needn't tell you . . . how appalled at Fielding's behaviour . . .

HEASLOP (*turning away*) It doesn't matter . . .

TURTON Well, all I can tell you is that you will have a chance to even the score in court.

HEASLOP (*harshly*) . . . this will have to come to trial? There is no possibility of . . .

TURTON Of their wriggling out of it? Certainly not. Set your mind at rest, my dear Heaslop. Of course there will be a trial.

HEASLOP . . . I didn't mean that . . .

TURTON And remember that we'll all be behind you . . .

HEASLOP (*more calmly*) Collector Sahib, I've been thinking . . .

TURTON (*reassuringly*) Perhaps I shouldn't be saying this, but of course we all know what the verdict will . . . well, let me leave it at this; we will back you every step of the way and when you speak from the magistrate's bench, you will be speaking for all of us.

HEASLOP But that's just it, sir . . . I don't think we should decide beforehand . . . I mean . . . (*he swallows hard and straightens up*) What I mean is, I don't think I should try this case.

TURTON We all understand your feelings, my boy, but they mustn't stand in your way at a time like this.

HEASLOP (*with difficulty, embarrassed at seeming "noble"*) Oh it's not my feelings so much . . . it's well, I don't think it would be fair . . . I mean, not really *just* . . .

MRS. TURTON (*in a high incredulous voice*) Not try the case?

HEASLOP I mean, I'm an interested party . . . don't you see?

BURTON But if you don't who will . . . ?

TURTON (*seriously*) Burton is right, Heaslop. What is the alternative?

HEASLOP (*quietly*) I'll have to hand it over to my deputy.

MRS. MCBRYDE (*hysterically*) Your deputy! An *Indian!* You'd allow an *Indian* . . .

TURTON Please, Mrs. McBryde . . .

HEASLOP Yes, I'm afraid so. I'll have to ask Das to take over.

CALLENDAR Heaslop, are you serious?

HEASLOP I was never more serious in my life. Das is a . . . is a good man. I've been training him for some time. He's sound, and . . . and loyal . . .

MRS. MCBRYDE None of them are loyal!

CALLENDAR You realize what's going to happen?

FLETCHER There could be bloodshed!

MRS. COLLIN Your own mother may be involved.

HEASLOP I'm sorry . . .

TURTON (*severely*) Heaslop, I must ask you to reconsider.

HEASLOP I'm afraid I really can't reconsider this decision, sir. I couldn't . . . (*firmly*) Well, I couldn't continue with my job here if I did. It's . . . well, justice, you see . . .

MRS. MCBRYDE Justice from an *Indian*?

HEASLOP (*unemphatically*) From *us*, Mrs. McBryde.

TURTON We won't try and persuade you further, Heaslop. We're all disturbed.

HEASLOP Thank you, Collector Sahib. I agree, that's best.

TURTON Yes, you think it over. Discuss it with your mother if you like and come and let me know your final decision.

> TURTON *turns to leave the room. The rest of the group breaks up, too, some for the verandah, some for the bar, a couple stand talking quietly at the door.*

HEASLOP (*walking towards his mother.* MRS. MOORE *pays no attention to him*) Mother, you do understand, don't you? Mother, I'm sorry. (*pause*) Adela was asking for you. Will you see her?

MRS. MOORE I would prefer not.

HEASLOP I know it's difficult for you, but she's so afraid. She needs reassurance from you.

MRS. MOORE That she made no mistake? She expects reassurance from me?

81

HEASLOP Oh, there's no mistake. She is quite sure. But she is frightened, and can't seem to stop crying. Oh, if only you'd been with her . . .

MRS. MOORE I was with her . . .

HEASLOP I mean, in the cave as a witness.

MRS. MOORE Those caves have no witnesses. It was pitch dark, anyway.

HEASLOP But nothing would have happened.

MRS. MOORE You cannot have her arrogance without something happening.

HEASLOP Arrogance? Adela arrogant? Why, she's the most modest creature in the world . . . all she wanted was to be useful and do some good.

MRS. MOORE Exactly. Arrogance.

HEASLOP And even now . . . even when she's so ill, she's worried about the trouble to others.

MRS. MOORE (laughs harshly) You see?

HEASLOP Mother, I don't see at all.

MRS. MOORE If you don't see, you don't see. The Professor told us . . . warned us . . . that there was nothing to see at the caves except with the inner eye. (turning to RONNY suddenly) Is she so special that she cannot come to terms?

HEASLOP Come to terms with what?

MRS. MOORE With India. With herself. And she worries about causing trouble. Ronny, you have always asked such silly questions.

HEASLOP Perhaps it was just that you couldn't answer them. Adela could . . . she was always clear, definite . . . it was the first thing about her that I really . . .

MRS. MOORE I suppose you will marry her after all?

HEASLOP Mother! What an extraordinary thing to say! How could I let her down now? We'll be married in the hills this summer as we planned.

MRS. MOORE Love in the heat. Marriage in the hills. Such a fuss! Marriage, marriage. The human race would have become a single person centuries ago if marriage were any use. But it is only an excuse because you are all too frightened to love. Of *love*. So you get married and talk a lot of rubbish about love . . . love in a church, love in a cave, as if there is the slightest difference.

HEASLOP   Mother, will you please tell me what you are talking about?

MRS. MOORE   About the small, kind people. I wish for their happiness. I told Dr. Aziz so . . . in our mosque and at the caves. The ones that can love.

HEASLOP (*hurt and angry*)   Love . . . you talk so much of love . . . vague, irresponsible . . . some young man in a mosque . . .

MRS. MOORE   It sounds vague, I dare say . . . universal love . . .

HEASLOP   You could have turned some of that famous love towards the people closer to you . . . things might have been different . . . *I* might have been different . . .

MRS. MOORE   And what about me? Have I no rights? Am I to be bothered eternally?

HEASLOP (*in exasperation*)   Mother, for heaven's sake, what do you want?

MRS. MOORE (*equally sharp*)   What do I want? I want to go home.

HEASLOP (*almost giving up, wearily*)   Yes, I'm sorry. I'll take you home now.

MRS. MOORE   I mean home to England.

HEASLOP   England? But you can't . . . There will be the trial in a few weeks, you'll have to give evidence.

MRS. MOORE   *Have to?* I have nothing to do with your ludicrous law courts. I will not be dragged in at all.

HEASLOP   I thought you would want to give evidence . . . to help . . . to help *Adela*.

MRS. MOORE   And listen to those endless, foolish questions? Was he in the cave, and were you in the cave and on and on . . . and Unto us a Son is born, unto us a Child is given . . . love again you see . . . and am I good and is he bad and are we saved? (*pause*) And ending every-

83

thing, the echo. That echo is India, after all. The end of all our pathetic dreams. Boum . . . Nothing . . . good or bad . . . love and hate and terror . . . all one . . .

HEASLOP   You must rest and then, you'll see, you'll feel much better . . . But I do wish . . . (*pathetically*) . . . It wouldn't be long. Another few weeks, and the trial. That is all.

MRS. MOORE   No, I have a lot of thinking to do, but even if I were not busy I would not help you to torture him for what he never did.

HEASLOP (*shocked, slowly*)   Mother, if you know anything in the prisoner's . . . in his favour, you must say so. It is your duty.

MRS. MOORE (*cynically*)   One knows people's characters, as you call them. I feel it is not the kind of thing he could do.

HEASLOP   That is no defence.

MRS. MOORE   None.

HEASLOP   Have you no evidence . . . concrete evidence?

MRS. MOORE   None.

HEASLOP   Then, Mother . . .

MRS. MOORE (*scornfully*)   Evidence.

HEASLOP   Then, you're being most inconsiderate to Adela . . .

MRS. MOORE   Why should I worry about her when everything I have ever believed in turns out to be meaningless . . . the good, small, loving people.

HEASLOP   Please . . . Mother . . . please listen . . . (*with difficulty*) I've never asked you . . . this sort of thing before . . . we've never been close . . . but for Adela, whom I . . . (*with great embarrassment*) whom I love (MRS. MOORE *laughs abruptly, and* HEASLOP *continues in a hopeless voice*) Won't you come and see her at least?

MRS. MOORE   No, Ronny, I will not. (*he turns away in despair*) I wish only to be left in peace to live out my days knowing what I now know.

HEASLOP (*exhausted*)   Very well, Mother, very well . . .

MRS. MOORE (*in a monotone*) Not justice, peace, retribution, goodness . . .

HEASLOP Oh Mother . . .

MRS. MOORE Just some part of the truth . . . if it is the truth . . .

HEASLOP You really must rest. It will all work out. Come, we'll go home.

MRS. MOORE (*standing up briskly*) Yes, Ronny. Yes. I am going home now.

CURTAIN

ACT THREE

The scene is a very simply arranged tropical court-room—a colonial magistrate's court, consequently there is no jury stand. There are slatted doors on each side of the stage, leading to the verandahs where crowds of spectators gather during the trial. At the back of the room is a low dais on which an imposing wooden chair and table are for the magistrate. On the wall above the dais is draped a Union Jack, and immediately below it a large tinted photograph of King George V and Queen Mary in their Durbar robes. Two tables, with several chairs around them, face the dais—these are for the defence lawyers and the prosecutors. Wooden benches without backs are set out for the public. The witness box is set on one side between the benches and the dais.

When the curtain rises a very young and extra-ordinary beautiful INDIAN SERVANT *is sitting cross-legged against the back wall, on the magistrate's dais. He is naked to the waist, wears a white muslin loin-cloth, is bare-headed. Around the big toe of one bare foot is wound the string of the punkah. The string stretches from his toe up to the ceiling, passes over a pulley and connects with a long wooden pole which extends almost the width of the ceiling. The pole hangs by three or four ropes attached to iron rings in the ceiling, and from the pole hangs a strip of cloth the same length as the pole. As the* YOUNG MAN *twitches his toe the cloth and pole swing slowly over the magistrate's dais, the lawyer's tables, the first few benches, and back again, creating a slight breeze. Throughout this act the* YOUNG MAN *continues to work the punkah, displaying no interest whatever in the court proceedings. His only action is to pause occasionally, change the string from the big toe of one foot to the big toe of the other, and then to carry on with his fanning.*

MISS QUESTED *sits on one of the benches, huddled over, and sobbing spasmodically. Beside her* HEASLOP *stands embarrassed and worried trying every now and again to comfort her. A couple of the* LADIES *from the Club sit beside her, soothing and sympathizing.*

QUESTED I'm so sorry ... I'm behaving in an appalling way, but I can't seem to help it.

MRS. CALLENDAR My dear, it's only to be expected.

QUESTED It's just my wretched nerves ... I'm so sorry.

MRS. TURTON Never mind, my dear, it will soon be over.

QUESTED It'll never be over ... not in all my life ...

MRS. BURTON Is there nothing we can do?

QUESTED No, thank you, I seem to be able to do nothing for myself.

MRS. TURTON Now you're forbidden to talk like that. You're wonderful.

MRS. CALLENDAR Yes, indeed you are.

QUESTED Oh you've all been so kind to me ... it's just that I dread the idea of giving evidence. If only I could somehow get out of ... no, I'm ashamed to have mentioned it; please forgive me ...

MRS. TURTON What you need, my dear, is something to give you strength, something to steady you. Did you have any breakfast?

MISS QUESTED *shakes her head.*

88

I'm going to get you some brandy.

QUESTED I don't think it will really help.

HEASLOP That's not a bad idea. Did you bring some down to the court, Mrs. Turton?

MRS. TURTON I should think I did. Champagne, too, but that's for after.

MRS. TURTON *leaves*.

QUESTED (*pathetically*) Ronny, my echo has come back again. Badly.

HEASLOP (*helplessly*) Poor girl . . . It seemed like a good idea to get here early and avoid the crowds but perhaps we should have let you rest at home.

MRS. BURTON How about some aspirin?

QUESTED It's not a headache, it is an echo.

MRS. BURTON (*getting up busily*) Well, try some aspirin anyway.

QUESTED (*as* MRS. BURTON *is leaving the room*) Ronny, I'm sure to break down.

HEASLOP You won't. You'll be strong.

QUESTED If I do break down, it is of no consequence. It would matter in some trials, not in this. I put it to myself in the following way; I can behave as I like, cry, be absurd, I am sure to get my verdict. Unless Mr. Das is most frightfully unjust.

HEASLOP No, he's all right. Remember, he's my old deputy. He's all right . . . if any of them are.

QUESTED You mean he's more frightened of acquitting than convicting because if he acquits he'll lose his job. (*she breaks down again*)

HEASLOP No . . . no.

QUESTED Oh, Ronny, I'm so sorry . . . how can I repay you? How can one repay when one has nothing to give? What is the use of personal relationships when everyone brings less and less to them? We ought to go back in the desert for centuries and try and get good. I want to begin at the beginning. I'm not fit for personal relationships. I'm . . .

> *He tries to put an arm round her to comfort her.*
> *She breaks away abruptly.*

Don't touch me! Please. I'm all right, really. I just need some air.

> *She gets up quickly, and keeping well away from*
> HEASLOP, *walks to the door and goes out.* HEASLOP
> *follows her.* FIELDING, *who has come in on the other*
> *side and has heard the last part of her speech,*
> *advances thoughtfully. He is followed by* GODBOLE.

FIELDING It does seem quite extraordinary. She always seemed such a dry sensible sort of girl . . . the last person wrongfully to accuse an Indian. Don't you think so, Godbole?

GODBOLE You are asking me to decide if Miss Quested acted wrongfully?

FIELDING (*surprised*) It hadn't occurred to me that it might be a question in your mind. Have you any doubts of his innocence?

> GODBOLE *says nothing and after a moment* FIELD-
> ING *continues more harshly.*

You will have to answer on the witness stand. What do you think. Is Dr. Aziz innocent or guilty?

GODBOLE That is for the court to decide. The verdict will be in strict accordance with the evidence, I make no doubt.

FIELDING Yes, but what's your personal opinion? Here's a man we both like and greatly esteem. Would he or would he not do such a thing?

GODBOLE Ah, that is a different question, from your previous one, and also more difficult: I mean difficult in our philosophy. Dr. Aziz is a most worthy young man, I have a great regard for him; but I think you are asking me whether the individual can commit good actions or evil actions, and that is rather difficult for us.

FIELDING (*impatient*) I ask you, did he or did he not do it? Well I know he didn't and from that I start. But if he is innocent, what actually happened? It couldn't be malice on Miss Quested's part? ... She has certainly had some appalling experience. But you, Godbole, you say, Oh no ... because good and evil are the same.

GODBOLE (*unruffled*) No, not exactly, please, according to our philosophy. Because nothing can be performed in isolation. All perform a good action when one is performed, and when an evil action is performed, all perform it.

FIELDING But you're always evading the issue.

GODBOLE (*interrupting gently*) To illustrate my meaning, let me take the case in point as an example. I am told that an evil action was performed in the Marabar Hills, and that a highly esteemed English lady became seriously ill in consequence. My answer to that is this: that action was performed by Dr. Aziz. (*pause*) It was performed by the guide. (*pause*) It was performed by you. (*he looks down, smiling*) It was performed by me. And by my students. It was even performed by the lady herself. When evil occurs, it expresses the whole of the universe. Similarly when good occurs.

FIELDING (*exasperated*) And similarly when suffering occurs, and so on and so forth.

GODBOLE Excuse me, you are once again changing the basis of our discussion. We were discussing good and evil. Suffering is merely a matter for the individual.

FIELDING Merely?

GODBOLE If a young lady has sunstroke, that is of no significance to the universe. Oh no, not at all. Oh, no, not at all. Not the least. It is an isolated matter, it only concerns herself. If she thought her head did not ache, she would not be ill, and that would end it. But it is far otherwise in the case of good and evil. They are not what we think them, they are what they are, and each of us has contributed to them both.

FIELDING You know you *are* preaching that good and evil are the same.

GODBOLE Oh no, excuse me once again. Good and evil are different, as their names imply. But in my humble opinion, they are both aspects of my Lord. He is present in the one, absent in the other, and the difference between presence and absence is great . . . as great as my feeble mind can grasp. Yet absence implies presence. Absence is not non-existence. And we are therefore entitled to repeat (*he bursts into a snatch of song—the same as the one he sang at the tea party*) or, "Come, come, come, come."

FIELDING (*in despair*) Don't you care what happens to Aziz?

GODBOLE It has already happened. Guilty or innocent, it doesn't matter. The change is made and all our lives are changed with it. We cannot escape that.

FIELDING (*restlessly*) I can only hope that our defence counsel Amritrao doesn't share your views.

GODBOLE He is highly respected in Calcutta. A very clever man.

FIELDING (*eagerly*) Do you know him? Is he good? I was hoping very much to have a few words with him before the trial.

GODBOLE He is most probably resting. He came up on the night train. I do not know him but I have no doubt he will give of his best to the case.

FIELDING Oh I dare say.

> *Enter* HAMIDULLAH, *a plump middle-aged man, dressed in orthodox Muslim clothes—tight jodhpurs, a long jacket buttoned to the throat, with a stiff stand-up collar of the same material, a black, felt Muslim cap. He is an emotional man, an old friend of Aziz, his strong feelings often carry him into impolitic scenes.*

Ah, Hamidullah!

HAMIDULLAH   My dear Fielding.

FIELDING   Have you brought Amritrao with you?

HAMIDULLAH   He stopped in my chambers for a few moments to make some notes.

FIELDING   Do you think he is the right man?

HAMIDULLAH   You will see he is our only hope.

FIELDING   I know he has a great reputation professionally and personally. But I have heard that he is notoriously anti-British.

HAMIDULLAH (*with emotion*)   What are we to do? We must hit with all our strength. I would gladly have defended Aziz alone, but when I knew that his . . . private papers are to be read in court . . . letters, photographs of his wife to be shown . . . think of the insult to a fine Muslim lady, a purdah lady! . . . When I saw that his reputation would be damaged beyond all hope, then I said to myself Amritrao is the man to clear this up. Let them take warning. Amritrao will show them.

FIELDING   Well, in any case, we are bound to win, there's nothing else we can do. She will never be able to substantiate the charge.

HAMIDULLAH (*warmly, shaking* FIELDING's *hand*)   At a crisis you English really are unequalled.

FIELDING   My dear Hamidullah, I don't suppose I shall have the opportunity of speaking to Aziz, but if you have the chance give him my love, and tell him, whatever happens, to keep calm.

HAMIDULLAH   My dear Fielding, you actually *are* on our side against your own people?

FIELDING   Yes. Definitely. Although I regret having to take sides.

> *From one side of the stage, some* COURT SERVANTS *bring in straight-backed chairs for the English people, and range them in front of the benches.*
>
> MISS QUESTED, HEASLOP, *the* CALLENDARS, MCBRYDES, *and* TURTONS *start filing in to take their places. From the other side* AMRITRAO, *a tall, grey-haired,*

93

handsome man, comes in. FIELDING *starts to go up to him, but is immediately diverted by the arrival of* AZIZ *looking worn and beaten, between* TWO GUARDS.

AZIZ Fielding! My friend ... my friend ... don't desert me ...

He is silenced and led to his place. FIELDING *unable to speak makes the gesture of a Muslim salaam just as he did in the first act.* AZIZ, *staring at him, suddenly smiles, relaxes, then responds as he did before.* HAMIDULLAH *and* AMRITRAO *sit at the defence table.* MCBRYDE *and an* ASSISTANT *in uniform at the prosecution table. The* PUBLIC *pushes in and finds places, jammed together on the benches. They are mostly men dressed in white shirts hanging outside their wide white pyjamas.* PEOPLE *stand in bunches at each door, and when any door swings partly open, the* CROWDS *outside can be seen too. Everyone stands as* MR. DAS, *the magistrate, a small timid man walks on to the platform. He wears western clothes, looks nervously around. Sits down. Everyone sits.* DAS *signals to the prosecution table.* MCBRYDE *gets up with some notes in his hand. The trial begins.*

MCBRYDE Well, sir, we are here today to deal with a crime of the most revolting sort. In consideration of Miss Quested I am going to recount the facts as briefly as possible ... I will make no moral or emotional appeal, for the facts themselves are painfully clear and require no elaboration. On April the third, of this year, Miss Quested and her friend Mrs. Moore were invited to a tea party at the house of the Principal of the Government College of Chandrapore, Mr. Fielding. It was at this entertainment that the prisoner first met Miss Quested and it was on this occasion that he conceived his intentions concerning her. He then invited Miss

94

Quested and the other guests at the tea party . . . Mrs. Moore and Professor Godbole . . . as well as his host, Mr. Fielding, to a picnic that he would arrange at the Marabar Caves in the Marabar Hills. In the course of our evidence we will show that the prisoner is a man of loose life, that documents found on him at the time of his arrest will testify to the state of his mind and the lasciviousness of his thoughts on the day of the picnic . . . (*looks up from his notes, regretfully*) We want to keep these proceedings as clean as possible, so I hope you will understand me when I say what I believe to be a general truth. The darker races are physically attracted to the fairer, but not vice versa. This is not a matter for bitterness, nor is it a matter for abuse. It is merely a fact which any scientific observer will confirm. (*pause to look back to his notes*)

VOICE (*from the* CROWD) Even when the lady is so uglier than the gentleman?

> *A burst of laughter mixed with horrified exclamations greets this question.* DAS *raps the table for order.*

DAS Turn that man out!

> TWO GUARDS *grab the nearest* MAN, *who has said nothing, and push him out of the court room.* MISS QUESTED *has buried her face in her hands.*

MRS. TURTON Do you feel faint, Adela?

QUESTED I never feel anything else. I shall get through.

CALLENDAR (*as order is gradually restored*) I must have better arrangements than this made for my patient. Why can't she have a seat on the platform? She gets no air.

DAS I shall be happy to accommodate Miss Quested with a chair up here in view of the particular circumstances of her health.

> *The* COURT SERVANTS *carry all the chairs on to the platform and the entire* PARTY *follow* MISS QUESTED *up and settle themselves around her.*

95

MRS. TURTON That's better.

CALLENDAR Thoroughly desirable change for several reasons. (*he pinches his nose suggestively*) Right, McBryde, go ahead now. Sorry to have interrupted you.

MCBRYDE Are you all right yourselves?

LADIES Thank you, yes. Much better.

TURTON Go on, Mr. Das, we are not here to disturb you.

DAS *signals nervously to* MCBRYDE.

MCBRYDE To continue. Even at Mr. Fielding's tea party the prisoner's manner to Miss Quested was offensive and familiar. Mr. Heaslop, when he arrived to fetch the ladies, found Miss Quested left alone with the Indians. He will testify that the prisoner's behaviour on this occasion was pushing and unnatural. This brings us to . . .

AZIZ *drops his head into his hands.*

HAMIDULLAH (*with angry irony*) Possibly my client, too, has nerves. Can he, too, be accommodated on the platform? Even Indians feel unwell sometimes, though naturally Major Callendar, being in charge of a Government hospital, does not think so.

MRS. TURTON (*loudly*) Another example of their exquisite sense of humour.

They all stare at DAS *aggressively.*

DAS (*agitated*) That is quite enough. Mr. Hamidullah. We will have no more interruptions of such an impertinent sort. Please resume, Superintendent.

AMRITRAO Excuse me. (*he has a strong Oxford accent*) We object to the presence of so many European ladies and gentlemen on the platform. They will have the effect of intimidating our witnesses. Their place is with the rest of the public in the body of the hall.

Pause, while the EUROPEANS *exchange looks.*

We have no objection to Miss Quested remaining on the platform, since she is unwell; we shall extend every courtesy to her throughout, despite the scientific truths revealed to us by the District Superintendent of Police. But we do object to the others.

CALLENDAR Oh cut the cackle and let's have the verdict.

DAS (*ducking his head behind some papers*) I agree to that. It was only to Miss Quested that I gave permission to sit up here. Her friends should be so excessively kind as to climb down.

HEASLOP Well done, Das. Quite right.

MRS. TURTON Climb down, indeed, what incredible impertinence!

TURTON Now, now, my dear, do come quietly.

CALLENDAR My patient can't be left unattended.

DAS Do you object to the Civil Surgeon remaining, Mr. Amritrao?

AMRITRAO I should object. A platform confers authority.

TURTON Even when it's one foot high? Well, never mind. Come along everyone. There's no point in making a fuss.

DAS (*greatly relieved*) Thank you very much, sir. Thank you, Mr. Heaslop. Thank you, ladies.

They all return with their chairs to their former position. MISS QUESTED *moves down with them.*

MCBRYDE Well, once again, to resume. I had come, I think, to the question of what I will call the prisoner's dupes. On April 13th, the day of the picnic, the ladies were driven to the railway station in time to catch the early train to Marabar. There they were met by the prisoner, his servants, and guides. Mr. Fielding, who was to join them at the station, had been asked to bring Professor Godbole with him. We will show that doubtless *some persuasion* was used to enable Professor Godbole to delay Mr. Fielding long enough to miss the train. I have here a plan of the Marabar Hills, showing the route that the party took. The picnic site is marked with a cross. (*he shows* DAS *the map*) Just here, in front of the Buddhist Cave.

DAS Not Buddhist, I think. Jain . . .

HAMIDULLAH In which cave is the offence alleged? The Buddhist or the Jain?

DAS All the Marabar Caves are Jain.

HAMIDULLAH That is not what the Superintendent said.

MCBRYDE No doubt the point is of vital archaeological interest. But at the moment all Mr. Das needs to know is that the offence took place in the cave that I have marked here. Miss Quested entered the cave and the prisoner followed her to make his premeditated assault. It was dark. He grabbed her field-glasses. The strap broke and she was able to escape his advances. She ran down this gully, marked here, through cactuses, and reached the road at this point. We will call Mrs. Callendar to testify to the condition of Miss Quested when she was found and brought back to Chandrapore, and we will produce documents both ladies signed on their arrival. Finally, we will produce witnesses to the finding of the field-glasses with the broken strap on the prisoner at the time of his arrest. I have little more to add at present. The facts will show the prisoner to be one of those individuals who have led a double life. He has pretended to be a respectable member of society, has even managed to get a Government position. If the defence calls character witnesses I beg you to remember that they, too, were probably taken in by his duplicity. He is now entirely vicious and beyond redemption, I am afraid. He behaved most cruelly, most brutally, to another of his guests, another English lady. In order to get rid of her, and leave him free for his crime, he crushed her into a cave among his servants. However, that is by the way.

AZIZ (*breaking out in a high, horrified voice*) Mrs. Moore! He is speaking of Mrs. Moore . . . she was my friend . . . once she told me . . .

DAS Quiet . . .

HAMIDULLAH (*yelling*) Mrs. Moore! What is this? Is my client charged with murder as well as rape? Who is this second English lady?

AZIZ I told you I met Mrs. Moore in the mosque. She was my friend.

HAMIDULLAH Mrs. Moore? Do you speak of Mrs. Moore?

MCBRYDE I don't propose to call her.

HAMIDULLAH You don't because you can't. You have smuggled her out of the country! She is Mrs. Moore, she would have proved his innocence! She was on our side, she was poor India's friend!

DAS (*trying to keep order*) You could have called her yourself. Neither side called her, neither must quote her as evidence.

HAMIDULLAH She was kept from us until too late . . . I learn too late . . . this is English justice. Here is your British Raj! Give us back Mrs. Moore . . .

DAS Order! I insist on order!

HAMIDULLAH Give us Mrs. Moore for five minutes only, and she will save my friend, she will save the name of his sons. Don't rule her out, Mr. Das. Take back those words as you yourself are a father. Tell me where they have put her . . .

HEASLOP (*dryly*) If the point is of any interest, my mother should have reached Aden by now.

HAMIDULLAH Imprisoned by you there because she knew the truth!

AMRITRAO *tries to calm him, but he is out of control.*

I don't care. I ruin my career, no matter. We are all to be ruined one by one.

DAS This is no way to defend your case, Mr. Hamidullah.

HAMIDULLAH I am not defending a case, nor are you trying one. We are both of us slaves. (*Thumps table.*)

DAS Mr. Hamidullah, I have already warned you, and unless you sit down I shall have to exercise my authority.

HAMIDULLAH Do so, do so by all means. This trial is a farce. I am going.

> *Flings his paper on the table in front of* AMRITRAO. *Walks to the door. In a sudden silence, histrionically, but with intense passion.*

Aziz, Aziz, my dear friend . . . farewell forever!

> *Exits amid excited murmurs from the* CROWD *outside and shouts of "Mrs. Moore! Mrs. Moore!"*

AMRITRAO I apologize for my colleague. He is an intimate friend of our client and his feelings have carried him away.

DAS (*severely*) Mr. Hamidullah will have to apologize in person.

AMRITRAO Exactly, sir, he must. But we have just learned that Mrs. Moore had important evidence which she desired to give. She was hurried out of the country by her son before she could give it; and this unhinged Mr. Hamidullah . . . coming as it does upon an attempt to undermine the evidence of our only other European witness, Mr. Fielding, by casting aspersions on his character. Mr. Hamidullah would have said nothing had not Mrs. Moore been claimed as a witness for the police.

DAS An extraneous element is being introduced into this case. I must repeat that as a witness Mrs. Moore does not exist. Neither you Mr. Amritrao, nor Mr. McBryde, you, have any right to surmise what the lady would have said.

MCBRYDE (*wearily*) Well, I withdraw my reference. As it happens she left India at her own insistence, and had no wish to give evidence on either side.

AMRITRAO I have already withdrawn the reference for the defence. (*smiling*) Perhaps you can persuade the gentlemen outside to withdraw it too.

DAS I am afraid my powers do not extend so far.

MCBRYDE I take it, then, that I may call my first witness.

> DAS *nods, still smiling.*

Miss Quested, please step up here.

*While she is being sworn in in an inaudible under-
tone.*

In view of Miss Quested's ill health, I wish to ask the
indulgence of the court to present my questions in an
abbreviated form so that she may not be tired out with
preliminaries.

DAS   Proceed, Mr. McBryde. I will stop you if your exami-
nation seems irregular.

The crowd's chatter ceases.

MCBRYDE   I will ask you then, Miss Quested, whether it is
true that you met the prisoner at a tea party at the house
of Mr. Fielding?

QUESTED   Yes.

MCBRYDE   Was the suggestion to have a picnic, and the
invitation to it, extended by him on that occasion?

QUESTED   Yes.

MCBRYDE   The prisoner met you at the railway station on
the morning of April 13th, and since Mr. Fielding did
not join you in time to catch the train, the prisoner,
Mrs. Moore and you travelled on ahead to Marabar.

QUESTED   Yes . . . that is, with the guide and servants.

MCBRYDE   Yes, of course. Now when you arrived at Marabar, your party climbed to the caves, and at the picnic
site in front of the caves paused for some refreshment.

QUESTED   Oh, Dr. Aziz had gone to a great deal of trouble.
I was worried that it was too expensive for him.

MCBRYDE   Yes, yes. No doubt. Now, after the refreshment,
you and Mrs. Moore were shown into the first of the
caves.

QUESTED   Yes.

MCBRYDE   We will ignore the incident in that cave, and
will only ask you whether Mrs. Moore expressed any
wish to continue to the other caves with you.

QUESTED   No. She was tired after the first cave. She did

not want to go on. She sat on one of the red chairs. She was oddly silent.

MCBRYDE So the prisoner and the guide took you on to the next cave?

QUESTED Yes. It was higher up and around a sort of spur. It was set in the most wonderfully shaped of those rocks. No one else was present. We appeared to be alone.

MCBRYDE Very well. There is a ledge half-way up the spur, or broken ground rather, with caves scattered near the beginning of a gully.

QUESTED I know where you mean.

MCBRYDE You went alone into one of those caves?

QUESTED Yes, that is quite correct.

MCBRYDE And the prisoner followed you?

CALLENDAR (*loudly*) Now we've got him.

Silence. Everyone waits for MISS QUESTED *to speak.*

MCBRYDE The prisoner followed you, didn't he?

Silence.

QUESTED I was thinking . . .

MCBRYDE Did the prisoner follow you? Take your time, Miss Quested.

QUESTED I was thinking before I went into the cave . . . thinking about my . . . engagement, about Ronny.

MCBRYDE (*gently*) There is no need to go into all that, Miss Quested. It has no bearing on our case.

QUESTED Oh, but you see it has. I had been talking to Dr. Aziz about my engagement to be married. And Dr. Aziz had been telling me about his own marriage . . .

MCBRYDE Well, now, that might indeed have a bearing on our case. It confirms the nature of the prisoner's thoughts . . .

QUESTED (*sharply*) Mr. McBryde, I am concerned with the nature of my own thoughts. I remember I was climbing over a rock that resembled an inverted saucer . . . and I was thinking about Ronny . . . and about love . . . and suddenly . . .

MCBRYDE (*more severely*) We need not worry with all that, Miss Quested . . . It is the facts that we must determine. Did the prisoner follow you into the cave?

QUESTED May I have a moment before I reply? It's coming clear in my mind.

MCBRYDE Yes.

QUESTED I discovered . . . I discovered . . . inside me . . . The discovery was such a shock . . . I felt like a mountaineer whose rope had broken. (*appealingly*) Not to love the man one's going to marry! Love . . . Yes I was thinking . . . about India . . . and about love . . . (*in a suddenly shocked voice*) Oh . . . I remember . . . I remember now . . .

MCBRYDE (*harshly*) Miss Quested, did he or did he not follow you into the cave?

QUESTED I'm not . . . I am not quite sure.

MCBRYDE I beg your pardon?

QUESTED I cannot be sure . . .

MCBRYDE I didn't catch that answer, Miss Quested. You are on that ledge, and you have entered a cave. I suggest to you that the prisoner followed you.

> MISS QUESTED *shakes her head.*

What do you mean, please?

QUESTED (*in a loud, flat voice*) No.

DAS (*as whispering and muttering begins in the court*) What is it that you are saying? Speak up, please.

QUESTED I'm afraid that I have made a mistake.

DAS What nature of mistake?

QUESTED Dr. Aziz never followed me into the cave.

MCBRYDE (*very controlled*) Now, Miss Quested, let us go on. I will read you the words of the deposition which you made some hours later in the Club.

> *He searches on the table for a paper.*

DAS (*over increasing indignation in the court*) Excuse me, Mr. McBryde, you cannot go on, sir. I am speaking to the witness myself. And the public will be silent. If it continues to talk I'll have the court cleared. (*The talking ceases.*) Miss Quested, address your remarks to me. I am the magistrate in charge of this case. Please realize the extreme gravity of your words, and remember you speak on oath, Miss Quested.

QUESTED Dr. Aziz never . . .

CALLENDAR (*springing up and shouting*) I stop these proceedings on medical grounds . . .

DAS (*ignoring him*) Miss Quested, you withdraw the charge? Answer me.

QUESTED (*rigid, and on the verge of collapse*) I withdraw everything.

DAS Enough . . . sit down. Mr. McBryde, do you wish to continue in the face of this?

MCBRYDE (*to* MISS QUESTED) Are you mad?

DAS Don't question her, sir. You no longer have the right.

> *The tumult in the court grows and spreads to the crowds outside.*

MCBRYDE Give me time to consider . . .

AMRITRAO Mr. McBryde, you will have to withdraw. This becomes a scandal.

MCBRYDE (*nonchalantly, even insultingly*) Right, I withdraw. (*he flings the notes on the table*)

MRS. TURTON (*shouting*) He shall not! Call the other witnesses! We're none of us safe . . .

> HEASLOP *tries to restrain her, but she hits out at him and begins to scream indistinguishable insults at* MISS QUESTED, *who sits straight and impervious on a bench.*

DAS (*yelling above the noise and movement of the crowd*) The prisoner is released without one stain on his character. The question of costs will be decided elsewhere.

> *Tumult breaks loose. The* BRITISH *struggle out of the court as best they can while* AZIZ, *weeping,*

embraces FIELDING *and* AMRITRAO. *Then he is captured by the* SPECTATORS, *and is seen being carried shoulder high along the verandah. The shouting from outside increases. Only* MISS QUESTED *remains exactly as she was. As* FIELDING, *in the rear of the* CROWD, *reaches the door, he looks back to the empty courtroom, notices first the* YOUNG MAN *who is still working the punkah, then sees* MISS QUESTED. *After a moment of indecision he returns to stand near her.*

FIELDING   What are you doing, Miss Quested? You can't just sit there. (*silence*) Where are you going to go?

QUESTED   I don't know.

FIELDING   Well, you can't stay here, and you can't just wander about the streets. Where's the car you came in?

QUESTED   Oh, gone, I'm sure. Perhaps I can walk . . .

FIELDING   Walk? What madness . . . there'll probably be a riot . . . Why don't you keep with your own people?

QUESTED   Ought I to join them?

FIELDING   Well, you can't now. It's too late . . .

AZIZ's *voice from outside calls, "Fielding! Fielding! Don't leave me! Where are you?"*

I'm coming! Coming soon . . . I'll meet you at my house! (*he turns back to* MISS QUESTED) Look, if you like, you can take my carriage . . . you'll be safe in it . . . send it back any time tomorrow.

QUESTED   But where am I to go in it?

FIELDING   Where you like. How should I know your arrangements?

QUESTED   I can't go to Ronny's house . . . or the Club . . . I don't want to be a trouble to anyone . . .

FIELDING   (*incredulously*)   *Trouble?* Good God, after all this . . .

QUESTED   I mean, if there is a hotel or something.

FIELDING   There is no hotel, only the Traveller's Rest House and that's very primitive . . .

105

QUESTED   That doesn't matter. I shall stay there until I can make arrangements to leave India.

FIELDING (*bitterly*)   As simple as that. (*suddenly violent*) What in God's name have you been doing? Playing a game? Studying life? Or what?

QUESTED (*with no resentment*)   Have you any explanation for my extraordinary behaviour?

FIELDING   None. Why make such a charge if you were going to withdraw it?

QUESTED   Why indeed.

FIELDING   I ought to feel grateful to you, I suppose, since Aziz is saved, but . . .

QUESTED   No, I am the only one to feel grateful after today's miseries. My echo has gone . . . I call that sort of buzzing sound in my ears an echo. You see, I have been unwell ever since that expedition to the caves, and possibly before it.

FIELDING   How unwell?

> *She touches the side of her head and then shakes it.*

Yes, that was my first thought, on the day of the arrest: hallucination.

QUESTED (*humbly*)   Do you think that's what it was? But what would have given me an hallucination?

FIELDING (*shrugs*)   Can you remember when you first felt out of sorts?

QUESTED   When I came to tea with you, in that garden-house.

FIELDING   A somewhat unlucky party.

QUESTED   I wasn't unwell, exactly . . . it's too vague to describe—it's all mixed up with my private affairs. I enjoyed Professor Godbole's singing . . . but just about then a sort of sadness began . . . no, nothing as solid as sadness. I began to see . . . or rather, to *sense* . . . that all my life . . . oh, my principles, the things I believed in, my feelings, affections, education . . . anything . . .

all amounted to nothing at all. India was too big for me.

FIELDING (*interested*) But that's like the echo in the caves. Mrs. Moore described them in very much the same way.

QUESTED (*eagerly*) Did she? Well, yes. I was in that state of sadness before I went into the caves, and you suggest . . . it was an hallucination, the sort of thing . . . that makes some women think they've had a proposal of marriage when none has been made.

FIELDING You put it very honestly.

QUESTED I was brought up to be honest. It gets me nowhere. In a way that's my trouble. Some honesties are too great to be borne . . . But that still leaves me with the question of why.

FIELDING Possibly one has to destroy what one cannot cope with.

QUESTED You mean India?

FIELDING Or yourself in India, your life in India . . .

QUESTED Or love?

FIELDING (*kindly*) Well, it's all over now.

> *Enter* HAMIDULLAH, *exuberantly rushing to* FIELD-ING *with open arms, scarcely noticing* MISS QUESTED.

HAMIDULLAH My dear Fielding? What is keeping you? There is to be a celebration at my house, but Aziz refuses to move without you . . . Come along.

FIELDING Miss Quested has been explaining a little about her conduct this morning.

HAMIDULLAH Perhaps the age of miracles has returned. One must be prepared for anything, for everything, our philosophers say.

QUESTED (*timidly*) It must have seemed a miracle to the onlookers. The fact is that I realized before it was too late that I had made a mistake, and had just enough presence of mind to say so. That is all my extraordinary conduct amounts to.

HAMIDULLAH (*enraged*) All it amounts to, indeed. Speaking as a private individual in a purely informal conversation, I admired your conduct. But I am surprised by your attitude. Indeed, surprise is too weak a word. I see you drag my best friend into the dirt, damage his health and ruin his prospects in a way you cannot conceive owing to your ignorance of our society and religion, and then suddenly you get up in the witness-box: "Oh, no, Mr. McBryde, after all I am not quite sure, you may as well let him go." Am I mad? I keep asking myself. Is it a dream, and if so when did it start? Come, Fielding, let us leave this callous woman.

QUESTED (*turning away*) I can't dispute it. Please don't let me detain you. I should be going, anyhow. The crowd must have thinned by now.

HAMIDULLAH (*to her retreating back*) And don't forget, Miss Quested, there will be costs! You will have to pay! Amritrao has fixed the compensation at twenty thousand rupees!

> MISS QUESTED *stops for a second at this.* FIELDING *looks helplessly from one to the other, makes a move in her direction.*

FIELDING Wait. Someone must go with you . . . you can't go alone. Wait for me in my carriage . . . (*she walks out stiffly, without a word*) Hamidullah . . . this is preposterous. That girl . . . how can that girl pay such an enormous sum? It would ruin her . . .

HAMIDULLAH And what about our friend Aziz? Is he not ruined? These English are all much richer than they tell you. Think of Aziz, Fielding. Think of Aziz.

> *Enter* AZIZ, *very exhilarated, active, affectionate, bouncing about.*

AZIZ Who is thinking of me? Fielding, Hamidullah, think of me in my victory . . . I agree, think of Aziz.

FIELDING (*seriously*) I am thinking of you, Aziz. Now is

the time for congratulations and celebration. You are the one in a strong position.

AZIZ There'll be a general shifting of position in Chandrapore.

FIELDING And you and I will probably get promotions . . . they can't very well move us down, whatever their feelings.

AZIZ In any case we spend our holidays together, in Kashmir, possibly Persia, for I shall have plenty of money. (*cynically*) Paid to me on account of the injury sustained by my character. While with me you shall never spend a single anna. That is my wish, and as the result of my misfortunes it has come.

FIELDING (*ponderously*) You have won a great victory . . .

AZIZ I know, my dear chap, I know. Your voice need not become so solemn and anxious. I know what you are going to say next: "Let, oh let Miss Quested off paying, so that the English may say, Here is a native who has actually behaved like a gentleman; if it was not for his black face we would almost allow him to join our club." (*suddenly changing his tone to bitterness*) The approval of your compatriots no longer interests me, I have become anti-British, and ought to have done so sooner. It would have saved me numerous troubles.

FIELDING Including knowing me.

AZIZ Come, come, Fielding. Let us go to the party . . . imagine, I have to leave my other friends and the joyful crowds to come and fetch you myself.

FIELDING Aziz, I can't celebrate yet. There is still another injustice. Miss Quested is an honest girl, in spite of the trouble she has caused. Do let her off lightly. She must pay your costs, that's only fair, but don't treat her like a conquered enemy.

AZIZ Must we discuss this now, when the celebration is waiting?

FIELDING Yes. At least, I must. Aziz . . . look here . . .

AZIZ I am looking, though it gets a bit dark. I see Mr. Fielding to be a very nice chap and my best friend, but in some ways a fool. You think that by letting Miss Quested off easily I shall make a better reputation for myself and all Indians generally. No, no. It will be put down to weakness and an attempt to gain promotion officially.

HAMIDULLAH Quite right, quite right.

AZIZ As a matter of fact, I have just now decided to have nothing more to do with British India. I shall find a job in some Muslim state—Hyderabad, Bhopal . . . where Englishmen can no longer insult me. Don't counsel me otherwise.

FIELDING I have been talking to Miss Quested.

AZIZ I don't want to hear about it.

FIELDING But I'll tell you anyway. I learned something about her. That she is perfectly genuine, and very brave. When she saw she was wrong she pulled herself up with a jerk and said so. I want you to realize what that means. She could easily have got you convicted, and all her friends around her, the entire British Raj was pushing her forward. But she stops, and sends the whole thing to smithereens. In her place I should have been too scared. But she had the courage to stop. Do treat her considerately. She really mustn't get the worst of both worlds. Be merciful. Act like one of your six Mogul Emperors, or all the six rolled into one.

AZIZ Not even Mogul Emperors showed mercy until they received an apology.

FIELDING (*eagerly*) She'll apologize, if that's the trouble . . . I'm sure. Look, I'll make you an offer. Dictate to me whatever form of words you like and this time to-morrow I'll bring it back signed.

AZIZ "Dear Dr. Aziz, I wish you had come into the cave. I am an awful old hag and it is my last chance." Will she sign that?

FIELDING (*disgusted*) After that there is nothing to be said.
AZIZ Indeed there is nothing.
FIELDING Goodbye.

> *He moves to the door, hesitates, and turns back, taking a last chance.*

Aziz, please do it. I can't bear to see you put yourself in a squalid position.

> AZIZ *shakes his head.*

Do it for my sake, then. Or if not mine, then Mrs. Moore's.
AZIZ Is that what she would have wanted?
FIELDING I am sure of it.
AZIZ (*after a long pause*) You put it in the only way that I cannot refuse. For the sake of a friend, one must do anything.
FIELDING (*exultantly, rushing to shake his hand, embrace him*) I knew you would! I knew you would do it!
AZIZ (*coldly*) That I would behave like an English gentleman? Miss Quested shall go free, and you, Fielding, will be the hero of what you call both worlds, for I shall certainly explain that I do this at your request. I wish you luck of it. Come, Hamidullah, let us go to our party.
FIELDING And me? Are we no longer friends?
AZIZ You belong with Miss Quested. You cannot be with us at the same time.
FIELDING Why not? Aziz . . . why . . .
AZIZ We do not understand each other. We are on different sides, and until there is no question of sides, we cannot be friends.
FIELDING Why should we be ruled by such things . . . colour, or politics . . . . it is India that forces this on us . . .
AZIZ (*sadly*) You see, in the end even you say that. It is India . . . Yes, probably India will be blamed for all the

guilts, and perhaps it is to blame. India is a large country, it can probably absorb all those guilts and a great deal else as well. It can certainly absorb our friendship and make nothing of it.

FIELDING One day, when things are different . . .

AZIZ One day.

> *He and* HAMIDULLAH *leave through the doors that lead to where the crowd had gathered.* FIELDING *watches them go, then turns and exits the other way through the door that* MISS QUESTED *took. There is silence for a moment. The* YOUNG MAN *working the punkah continues to twitch his foot, staring without expression over the empty court room, as*

THE CURTAIN FALLS

WITHDRAWN

W9-BIA-329

Why not?

"It's nice, dear," Fly said to Babe. "I've still got you."

But not for all that long, she thought. Poor little chap, in six months or so he'll be fit to kill. At least he doesn't know it. She looked at him fondly, this foster child that now called her "Mum." He had picked it up, naturally enough, from the puppies, and it pleased her to hear it, now more than ever.

"Mum," said Babe.

"Yes, dear?"

"They've gone off to work sheep, haven't they?"

"Yes, dear."

"Because they're sheepdogs. Like you. You're useful to the boss, aren't you, because you're a sheepdog?"

"Yes, dear."

"Well, Mum?"

"Yes, dear?"

"Why can't I learn to be a sheep-pig?"

Knopf Paperbacks by the same author:

BABE
The Gallant Pig

DICK KING-SMITH

Illustrated by Mary Rayner

A KNOPF PAPERBACK
ALFRED A. KNOPF
NEW YORK

A KNOPF PAPERBACK PUBLISHED BY ALFRED A. KNOPF, INC.

Text copyright © 1983 by Dick King-Smith
Illustrations copyright © 1983 by Mary Rayner
Cover art © 1997 by Universal City Studios, Inc. Courtesy of MCA
Publishing Rights, a Division of MCA Inc. All rights reserved.
Cover painting by Wayne Parmenter

All rights reserved under International and Pan-American Copyright
Conventions. Published in the United States of America by Alfred A. Knopf,
Inc., New York. Distributed by Random House, Inc., New York. Originally
published in Great Britain in 1983 under the title *The Sheep Pig*. Published in
hardcover by Crown Publishers, Inc., in 1985.

http://www.randomhouse.com/

Library of Congress Cataloging-in-Publication Data
King-Smith, Dick.
Babe : the gallant pig.
Summary: A piglet destined for eventual butchering arrives at the farmyard, is
adopted by an old sheep dog, and discovers a special secret to success.
1. Children's stories, English.   [1. Pigs—Fiction.   2. Domestic Animals—
Fiction]   I. Rayner, Mary, ill.   II. Title.
PZ7.K5893Bab   1985   [Fic]   84-11429
ISBN 0-679-87393-7

First Knopf Paperback edition: April 1997
Printed in the United States of America
15 14 13 12 11 10

Contents

CHAPTER I

"Guess my weight"

"What's that noise?" said Mrs. Hogget, sticking her comfortable round red face out of the kitchen window. "Listen, there 'tis again, did you hear it, what a racket, what a row, anybody'd think someone was being murdered, oh dearie me, whatever is it, just listen to it, will you?"

Farmer Hogget listened. From the usually quiet valley below the farm came a medley of sounds: the oompah oompah of a brass band, the shouts of children, the rattle and thump of a skittle alley, and every now and then a very high, very loud, very angry-sounding squealing lasting about ten seconds.

Farmer Hogget pulled out an old pocket watch as big around as a saucer and looked at it. "Fair starts at two," he said. "It's started."

9

"I knows that," said Mrs. Hogget, "because I'm late now with all these cakes and jams and pickles and preserves as is meant to be on the Produce Stall this very minute, and who's going to take them there, I'd like to know, why you are, but afore you does, what's that noise?"

The squealing sounded again.

"That noise?"

Mrs. Hogget nodded a great many times. Everything that she did was done at great length, whether it was speaking or simply nodding her head. Farmer Hogget, on the other hand, never wasted his energies or his words.

"Pig," he said.

Mrs. Hogget nodded a lot more.

"I thought 'twas a pig, I said to meself that's a pig that is, only nobody round here do keep pigs, 'tis all sheep for miles about, what's a pig doing, I said to meself, anybody'd think they was killing the poor thing, have a look when you take all this stuff down, which you better do now, come and give us a hand, it can go in the back of the Land Rover, 'tisn't raining, 'twon't hurt, wipe your boots afore you comes in."

"Yes," said Farmer Hogget.

When he had driven down to the village and made his delivery to the Produce Stall, Farmer Hogget walked across the green, past the fortune tellers, the games of chance, the ferris wheel and the band, to the source of the squealing noise, which came every now and again from a small pen in a far corner, against the churchyard wall.

11

By the pen sat the Vicar, notebook in hand, a cardboard box on the table in front of him. On the pen hung a notice—'Guess my weight. Ten pence a shot.' Inside was a little pig.

As Farmer Hogget watched, a man leaned over and picked it out of the pen. He hefted it in both hands, frowning and pursing his lips in a considering way, while all the time the piglet struggled madly and yelled blue murder. The moment it was put down, it stopped. Its eyes, bright intelligent eyes, met the farmer's. They regarded one another.

One saw a tall thin brown-faced man with very long legs, and the other saw a small fat pinky-white animal with very short ones.

"Ah, come along, Mr. Hogget!" said the Vicar. "You never know, he could be yours for ten pence. Guess his weight correctly, and at the end of the day you could be taking him home!"

"Don't keep pigs," said Farmer Hogget. He stretched out a long arm and scratched its back. Gently, he picked it up and held it before his face. It stayed quite still and made no sounds.

"That's funny," said the Vicar. "Every time so far that someone has picked him up he's screamed his head off. He seems to like you. You'll have to take a guess."

12

Carefully, Farmer Hogget put the piglet back in the pen. Carefully, he took a ten-pence piece from his pocket and dropped it in the cardboard box. Carefully, he ran one finger down the list of guesses already in the Vicar's notebook.

"Quite a variation," said the Vicar. "Anything from twenty pounds to forty, so far." He wrote down "Mr. Hogget" and waited, pencil poised.

Once again, slowly, thoughtfully, the farmer picked the piglet up.

Once again, it remained still and silent.

"Thirty-one pounds," said Farmer Hogget. He put the little pig down again. "And a quarter," he said.

"Thirty-one and a quarter pounds. Thank you, Mr. Hogget. We shall be weighing the little chap at about half past four."

"Be gone by then."

"Ah well, we can always telephone you. If you should be lucky enough to win him."

"Never win nothing."

13

As he walked back across the green, the sound of the pig's yelling rang out as someone else took a guess.

"You never do win nothing," said Mrs. Hogget over tea, when her husband, in a very few words, had explained matters. "Though I've often thought I'd like a pig, we could feed 'un on scraps, he'd come just right for Christmas time, just think, two nice hams,

14

two sides of bacon, pork chops, kidneys, liver, chitterlings, trotters, save his blood for black pudding, there's the phone."

Farmer Hogget picked it up.

"Oh," he said.

CHAPTER 2

"There. Is that nice?"

In the farmyard, Fly, the black-and-white collie, was beginning to train her four puppies. For some time now they had shown an instinctive interest in anything that moved, driving it away or bringing it back, turning it to left or right, in fact herding it. They had begun with such things as passing beetles, but were now ready, Fly considered, for larger creatures.

She set them to work on Mrs. Hogget's ducks.

Already the puppies were beginning to move as sheepdogs do, seeming to creep rather than walk, heads held low, ears pricked, eyes fixed on the angrily quacking birds as they maneuvered them about the yard.

"Good boys," said Fly. "Leave them now. Here comes the boss."

The ducks went grumbling off to the pond, and the five dogs watched as Farmer Hogget got out of the

Land Rover. He lifted something out of a crate in the back, and carried it into the stables.

"What was that, Mum?" said one of the puppies.

"That was a pig."

"What will the boss do with it?"

"Eat it." said Fly. "When it's big enough."

"Will he eat us," said another, rather nervously, "when we're big enough?"

"Bless you," said his mother. "People only eat stupid animals. Like sheep and cows and ducks and chickens. They don't eat clever ones like dogs."

"So pigs are stupid?" said the puppies.

Fly hesitated. On the one hand, having been born and brought up in sheep country, she had in fact never been personally acquainted with a pig. On the other, like most mothers, she did not wish to appear ignorant before her children.

"Yes," she said. "They're stupid."

At this point there came from the kitchen window a long burst of words like the rattle of a machine gun, answered by a single shot from the stables, and Farmer Hogget emerged and crossed the yard toward the farmhouse with his loping stride.

"Come on," said the collie bitch. "I'll show you."

The floor of the stables had not rung to a horse's hoof for many years, but it was a useful place for storing things. The hens foraged about there, and sometimes laid their eggs in the old wooden mangers; the swallows built their nests against its roof beams with mud from the duck pond; and rats and mice lived happy lives in its shelter until the farm cats cut them short. At one end of the stables were two loose boxes with boarded sides topped by iron rails. One served as a kennel for Fly and her puppies. The other sometimes housed sick sheep. In there Farmer Hogget had put the piglet.

A convenient stack of straw bales allowed the dogs to look down into the box through the bars.

"There. Is that nice?"

"It certainly looks stupid," said one of the puppies, yawning. At the sound of the words the piglet glanced up quickly. He put his head to one side and regarded the dogs with sharp eyes. Something about the sight of this very small animal standing all by itself in the middle of the roomy loose box touched Fly's soft heart. Already she was sorry that she had said that pigs were stupid, for this one certainly did not appear to be so. Also there was something dignified about the way it stood its ground, in a strange place, confronted with strange animals. How

different from the silly sheep, who at the mere sight of a dog would run aimlessly about, crying "Wolf! Wolf!" in their empty-headed way.

"Hullo," she said. "Who are you?"

"I'm a Large White," said the piglet.

"Blimey!" said one of the puppies. "If that's a large white, what's a small one like?" And they all four sniggered.

"Be quiet!" snapped Fly. "Just remember that five minutes ago you didn't even know what a pig was." And to the piglet she said kindly, "I expect that's your breed, dear. I meant, what's your name?"

"I don't know," said the piglet.

"Well, what did your mother call you, to tell you apart from your brothers and sisters?" said Fly and then wished she hadn't, for at the mention of his family the piglet began to look distinctly unhappy. His little forehead wrinkled and he gulped and his voice trembled as he answered.

"She called us all the same."

"And what was that, dear?"

"Babe," said the piglet, and the puppies began to giggle until their mother silenced them with a growl.

"But that's a lovely name," she said. "Would you like us to call you that? It'll make you feel more at home."

"There. Is that nice?"

At this last word the little pig's face fell even further.

"I want my mum," he said very quietly.

At that instant the collie bitch made up her mind that she would foster this unhappy child.

"Go out into the yard and play," she said to the puppies, and she climbed to the top of the straw stack and jumped over the rail and down into the loose box beside the piglet.

"Listen, Babe," she said. "You've got to be a brave boy. Everyone has to leave their mother, it's all part of growing up. I did it, when I was your age, and my puppies will have to leave me quite soon. But I'll look after you. If you like." Then she licked his little snout with a warm rough tongue, her plumed tail wagging.

"There. Is that nice?" she said.

A little while later, Farmer Hogget came into the stables with his wife, to show her his prize. They looked over the loose box door and saw, to their astonishment, Fly curled around the piglet. Exhausted by the drama of the day, Babe lay fast asleep against his newfound foster parent.

"Well, will you look at that!" said Mrs. Hogget. "That old Fly, she'll mother anything, kittens, duck-lings, baby chicks, she's looked after all of them, now

'tis a pig, in't he lovely, what a picture, good thing he
don't know where he'll finish up, but he'll be big then
and we'll be glad to see the back of him, or the hams
of him, I should say, shan't we, wonder how I shall
get it all in the freezer?"

"Pity. Really," said Farmer Hogget absently.

Mrs. Hogget went back to her kitchen, shaking her
head all the way across the yard at the thought of her
husband's softheartedness.

22

"There. Is that nice?"

The farmer opened the loose box door, and to save the effort of a word, clicked his fingers to call the bitch out.

As soon as Fly moved the piglet woke and followed her, sticking so close to her that his snout touched her tail tip. Surprise forced Farmer Hogget into speech.

"Fly!" he said in amazement. Obediently, as always, the collie bitch turned and trotted back to him. The pig trotted behind her.

"Sit!" said Farmer Hogget. Fly sat. Babe sat. Farmer Hogget scratched his head. He could not think of anything to say.

CHAPTER 3

"Why can't I learn?"

By dark it was plain to Farmer Hogget that, whether he liked it or not, Fly had not four, but five children.

All the long summer evening Babe had followed Fly about the yard and buildings, aimlessly, it seemed to the watching farmer, though of course this was not the case. It was in fact a conducted tour. Fly knew that if this foster child was to be allowed his freedom and the constant reassurance of her company for which he obviously craved, he must quickly learn (and clearly he was a quick learner) his way about the place; and that he must be taught, as her puppies had been taught, how to behave like a good dog.

"A pig you may be, Babe," she had begun by saying, "but if you do as I tell you, I shouldn't be a bit surprised if the boss doesn't let you run about with us, instead of shutting you up. He's a kind man, the boss is."

24

"I knew that," said Babe, "when he first picked me up. I could feel it. I knew he wouldn't hurt me."

"You wait . . ." began one of the puppies, and then stopped suddenly at his mother's warning growl. Though she said nothing, all four of her children knew immediately by instinct what she meant.

"Wait for what?" said Babe.

"Er . . . you wait half a sec, and we'll take you round and show you everything," said the same puppy hastily. "Won't we, Mum?"

So Babe was shown all around the yard and the farm buildings, and introduced to the creatures who lived thereabouts, the ducks and chickens and other poultry, and the farm cats. He saw no sheep, for they were all in the fields.

Even in the first hour he learned a number of useful lessons, as the puppies had learned before him: that cats scratch and hens peck, that turning your back on the turkey cock means getting your bottom bitten, that chicks are not for chasing and eggs are not for eating.

"You do as I do," said Fly, "and you'll be all right."

She thought for a moment. "There is one thing though, Babe," she said, and she looked across at the back door of the farmhouse, "if I go in there, you stay

25

outside and wait for me, understand?"

"Aren't pigs allowed in there?" asked Babe.

"Not live ones," said one of the puppies, but he said it under his breath.

"No, dear," said Fly. Well, not yet anyway, she thought. But the way you're going on, I shouldn't be surprised at anything. Funny, she thought, I feel really proud of him, he learns so quick. Quick as any sheepdog.

That night the loose box in which Babe had first been put was empty. In the one next door, all six animals slept in the straw together. Though he did not tell his wife, Farmer Hogget had not had the heart to shut the piglet away, so happy was it in the company of the dogs.

At first the puppies had not been equally happy at the idea.

"Mum!" they said. "He'll wet the bed!"

"Nonsense," said Fly. "If you want to do anything, dear, you go outside, there's a good boy."

I nearly said, "There's a good pup," she thought. Whatever next!

In fact, in the days that followed, Babe became so doglike, what with coming when Fly came and sitting when Fly sat and much preferring dog's food

26

Becoming Dog Like
Imitates
creates
Dog
comdy
Play
Behaviour

to anything else he was offered, that Farmer Hogget caught himself half expecting, when he patted the piglet, that it would wag its tail. He would not have been surprised if it had tried to accompany Fly when he called her to go with him on his morning rounds, but it had stayed in the stables, playing with the puppies.

"You stay with the boys, Babe," Fly had said, "while I see to the sheep. I shan't be long."

"What's sheep?" the piglet said when she had gone.

The puppies rolled about in the straw.

"Don't you know that, you silly Babe?" said one.

"Sheep are animals with thick woolly coats."

"And thick woolly heads."

"And men can't look after them without the help of the likes of us," said the fourth.

"Why do they need you?" said Babe.

"Because we're sheepdogs!" they all cried together, and ran off up the yard.

Babe thought about this matter of sheep and sheepdogs a good deal during the first couple of weeks of his life on the Hoggets' farm. In that time Fly's puppies, now old enough to leave home, had been advertised for sale, and Fly was anxious to teach them all she could before they went out into the world. Daily she made them practice on the ducks, while Babe sat beside her and watched with interest. And daily their skills improved and the ducks lost weight and patience.

Then there came, one after another, four farmers, four tall long-legged men who smelled of sheep. And each picked his puppy and paid his money, while Fly sat and watched her children leave to start their working life.

As always, she felt a pang to see them go, but this time, after the last had left, she was not alone.

"It's nice, dear," she said to Babe. "I've still got you."

But not for all that long, she thought. Poor little chap, in six months or so he'll be fit to kill. At least he doesn't know it. She looked at him fondly, this foster child that now called her "Mum." He had picked it up, naturally enough, from the puppies, and it pleased her to hear it, now more than ever. *he knows*

"Mum," said Babe.

"Yes, dear?"

"They've gone off to work sheep, haven't they?"

"Yes, dear."

"Because they're sheepdogs. Like you. You're useful to the boss, aren't you, because you're a sheepdog?"

"Yes, dear."

"Well, Mum?"

"Yes, dear?"

"Why can't I learn to be a sheep-pig?" *watching + its train watching lessons*

29

CHAPTER 4

"You'm a polite young chap"

After the last of the puppies had left, the ducks heaved a general sigh of relief. They looked forward to a peaceful day and paid no attention when, the following morning, Fly and Babe came down to the pond and sat and watched them as they squattered and splattered in its soupy green depths. They knew that the old dog would not bother them, and they took no notice of the strange creature at her side.

"They'll come out and walk up the yard in a minute," said Fly. "Then you can have a go at fetching them back, if you like."

"Oh yes, please!" said Babe excitedly.

The collie bitch looked fondly at her foster child. Sheep-pig indeed, she thought, the idea of it! The mere sight of him would probably send the flock into the next county. Anyway, he'd never get near them on those little short legs. Let him play with the ducks

30

for a day or two and he'd forget all about it.

When the ducks did come up out of the water and marched noisily past the piglet, she half expected him to chase after them, as the puppies usually did at first; but he sat very still, he ears cocked, watching her.

"All right," said Fly. "Let's see how you get on. Now then, first thing is, you've got to get behind them, just like I have to with the sheep. If the boss wants me to go round the right side of them (that's the side by the stables there), he says 'Away to me.' If he wants me to go round the left (that's the side by the Dutch barn), he says 'Come by.' O.K.?"

"Yes, Mum."

"Right then. Away to me, Babe!" said Fly sharply.

At first, not surprisingly, Babe's efforts met with little success. There was no problem with getting around the ducks—even with his curious little seesawing canter he was much faster than they—but the business of bringing the whole flock back to Fly was not, he found, at all easy. Either he pressed them too hard and they broke up and fluttered all over the place, or he was too gentle and held back, and they waddled away in twos and threes.

"Come and have a rest, dear," called Fly after a while. "Leave the silly things alone, they're not worth upsetting yourself about."

31

"I'm not upset, Mum," said Babe. "Just puzzled. I mean, I told them what I wanted them to do but they didn't take any notice of me. Why not?"

Because you weren't born to it, thought Fly. You haven't got the instinct to dominate them, to make them do what you want.

"It's early days yet, Babe dear," she said.

"Do you suppose," said Babe, "that if I asked them politely . . ."

"Asked them politely! What an idea! Just imagine me doing that with the sheep—'please will you go through that gateway,' 'would you kindly walk into that pen?' Oh no, dear, you'd never get anywhere that way. You've got to tell 'em what to do, doesn't matter whether it's ducks or sheep. They're stupid and dogs are intelligent, that's what you have to remember."

"But I'm a pig."

"Pigs are intelligent too," said Fly firmly. Ask them politely, she thought. Whatever next!

What happened next, later that morning in fact, was that Babe met his first sheep.

Farmer Hogget and Fly had been out around the flock, and when they returned Fly was driving before her an old lame ewe, which they penned in the loose box where the piglet had originally been shut. Then they went away up the hill again.

Babe made his way into the stables, curious to meet this, the first of the animals that he planned one day to work with, but he could not see into the box. He snuffled under the bottom of the door, and from inside there came a cough and the sharp stamp of a foot, and then the sound of a hoarse complaining voice. "Wolves! Wolves!" it said. "They never do

33

leave a body alone. Nag, nag, nag all day long, go here, go there, do this, do that. What d'you want now? Can't you give us a bit of peace, wolf?"

"I'm not a wolf," said Babe under the door.

"Oh, I knows all that," said the sheep sourly. "Calls yourself a sheepdog, I knows that, but you don't fool none of us. You're a wolf like the rest of 'em, given half a chance. You looks at us, and you sees lamb chops. Go away, wolf."

"But I'm not a sheepdog either," said Babe, and he scrambled up the stack of straw bales and looked over the bars.

"You see?" he said.

"Well I'll be dipped," said the old sheep, peering up at him. "No more you ain't. What are you?"

"Pig," said Babe. "Large White. What are you?"

"Ewe," said the sheep.

"No, not me, you—what are you?"

"I'm a ewe."

Mum was right, thought Babe, they certainly are stupid. But if I'm going to learn how to be a sheep-pig I must try to understand them, and this might be a good chance. Perhaps I could make a friend of this one.

"My name's Babe," he said in a jolly voice. "What's yours?"

34

"Maaaaa," said the sheep.

"That's a nice name," said Babe. "What's the matter with you, Ma?"

"Foot rot," said the sheep, holding up a foreleg. "And I've got a nasty cough." She coughed. "And I'm not as young as I was."

"You don't look very old to me," said Babe politely.

A look of pleasure came over the sheep's mournful face, and she lay down in the straw.

"Very civil of you to say so," she said. "First kind word I've had since I were a little lamb," and she belched loudly and began to chew a mouthful of cud.

35

Though he did not quite know why, Babe said
nothing to Fly of his conversation with Ma. Farmer
Hogget had treated the sheep's foot and tipped a
potion down its protesting throat, and now, as
darkness fell, dog and pig lay side by side, their rest
only occasionally disturbed by a rustling from the
box next door. Having at last set eyes on a sheep,
Babe's dreams were immediately filled with the creatures, all lame, all coughing, all, like the ducks,
scattering wildly before his attempts to round them
up.

"Go here, go there, do this, do that!" he squeaked
furiously at them, but they took not a bit of notice,
until at last the dream turned to a nightmare, and they
all came hopping and hacking and maa-ing after him
with hatred gleaming in their mad yellow eyes.

"Mum! Mum!" shouted Babe in terror.

"Maaaaa!" said a voice next door.

"It's all right dear," said Fly, "it's all right. Was it a
nasty dream?"

"Yes, yes."

"What were you dreaming about?"

"Sheep, Mum."

"I expect it was because of that stupid old thing in
there," said Fly. "Shut up!" she barked. "Noisy old
fool!" And to Babe she said, "Now cuddle up, dear,

36

and go to sleep. There's nothing to be frightened of."

She licked his snout until it began to give out a series of regular snores. Sheep-pig indeed, she thought, why the silly boy's frightened of the things, and she put her nose on her paws and went to sleep.

Silliness of the Dream

Babe slept soundly the rest of the night, and woke more determined than ever to learn all that he could from their new neighbor. As soon as Fly had gone out on her rounds, he climbed the straw stack.

"Good morning, Ma," he said. "I do hope you're feeling better today?"

The old ewe looked up. Her eyes, Babe was glad to see, looked neither mad nor hateful.

"I must say," she said, "you'm a polite young chap. Not like that wolf, shouting at me in the middle of the night. Never get no respect from them, treat you like dirt they do, bite you soon as look at you."

"Do they really?"

"Oh ar. Nip your hocks if you'm a bit slow. And worse, some of them."

"Worse?"

"Oh ar. Ain't you never heard of worrying?"

"I don't worry much."

"No no, young un. I'm talking about sheep-worrying. You get some wolves as'll chase sheep and kill 'em."

"Oh!" said Babe, horrified. "I'm sure Fly would never do that."

"Who's Fly?"

"She's my m . . . she's our dog here, the one that brought you in yesterday."

"Is that what she's called? No, she bain't a worrier, just rude. All wolves is rude to us sheep, see, always have been. Bark and run and nip and call us stupid. We bain't all that stupid, we do just get confused. If only they'd just show a bit of common politeness, just treat us a bit decent. Now if you was to come out into the field, a nice well-mannered young chap like you, and ask me to go somewhere or do something, politely, like you would, why, I'd be only too delighted."

CHAPTER 5

"Keep yelling, young un"

Mrs. Hogget shook her head at least a dozen times.

"For the life of me I can't see why you do let that pig run all over the place like you do, round and round the yard he do go, chasing my ducks about, shoving his nose into everything, shouldn't wonder but what he'll be out with you and Fly moving the sheep about afore long, why don't you shut him up, he's running all his flesh off, he won't never be fit for Christmas, Easter more like, what d'you call him?"

"Just Pig," said Farmer Hogget.

A month had gone by since the Village Fair, a month in which a lot of interesting things had happened to Babe. The fact that perhaps most concerned his future, though he did not know it, was that Farmer Hogget had become fond of him. He liked to see the piglet pottering happily about the yard with

39

Fly, keeping out of mischief, as far as he could tell, if you didn't count moving the ducks around. He did this now with a good deal of skill, the farmer noticed, even to the extent of being able, once, to separate the white ducks from the brown, though that must just have been a fluke. The more he thought of it, the less Farmer Hogget liked the idea of butchering Pig.

The other developments were in Babe's education. Despite herself, Fly found that she took pleasure and pride in teaching him the ways of the sheepdog, though she knew that of course he would never be fast enough to work sheep. Anyway the boss would never let him try.

As for Ma, she was back with the flock, her foot healed, her cough better. But all the time that she had been shut in the box, Babe had spent every moment that Fly was out of the stables chatting to the old ewe. Already he understood, in a way that Fly never could, the sheep's point of view. He longed to meet the flock, to be introduced. He thought it would be extremely interesting.

"D'you think I could, Ma?" he had said.

"Could what, young un?"

"Well, come and visit you, when you go back to your friends?"

"Oh ar. You could do, easy enough. You only got

40

to go through the bottom gate and up the hill to the big field by the lane. Don't know what the farmer'd say though. Or that wolf."

Once Fly had slipped quietly in and found him perched on the straw stack.

"Babe!" she had said sharply. "You're not talking to that stupid thing, are you?"

"Well, yes, Mum, I was."

"Save your breath, dear. It won't understand a word you say."

"Bah!" said Ma.

For a moment Babe was tempted to tell his foster mother what he had in mind, but something told him to keep quiet. Instead he made a plan. He would wait for two things to happen. First, for Ma to rejoin the flock. And, after that, for market day, when both the boss and his mum would be out of the way. Then he would go up the hill.

Towards the end of the very next week the two things had happened. Ma had been turned out, and a couple of days after that Babe watched as Fly jumped into the back of the Land Rover, and it drove out of the yard and away.

Babe's were not the only eyes that watched its departure. At the top of the hill a cattle truck stood

41

half-hidden under a clump of trees at the side of the lane. As soon as the Land Rover had disappeared from sight along the road to the market town, a man jumped hurriedly out and opened the gate into the field. Another backed the truck into the gateway.

Babe meanwhile was trotting excitedly up the hill to pay his visit to the flock. He came to the gate at the bottom of the field and squeezed under it. The field was steep and curved, and at first he could not see a single sheep. But then he heard a distant drumming of hooves and suddenly the whole flock came galloping over the brow of the hill and down toward him. Around them ran two strange collies, lean silent dogs that seemed to flow effortlessly over the grass. From high above came the sound of a thin whistle, and in easy partnership the dogs swept around the sheep, and began to drive them back up the slope.

42

Babe initially trapped caught [handwritten annotation]

Despite himself, Babe was caught up in the press of jostling bleating animals and carried along with them. Around him rose a chorus of panting protesting voices, some shrill, some hoarse, some deep and guttural, but all saying the same thing.

"Wolf! Wolf!" cried the flock in dazed confusion.

Small by comparison and short in the leg, Babe soon fell behind the main body, and as they reached the top of the hill he found himself right at the back in company with an old sheep who cried "Wolf!" more loudly than any.

"Ma!" he cried breathlessly. "It's you!" *Babe finds MA* [handwritten annotation]

Behind them one dog lay down at a whistle, and in front the flock checked as the other dog steadied them. In the corner of the field the tailgate and wings of the cattle truck filled the gateway, and the two men waited, sticks and arms outspread.

43

Babe Learns
Babe Understands
Babe Makes a Decision —

"Oh hullo, young un," puffed the old sheep. "Fine day you chose to come, I'll say."

"What is it? What's happening? Who are these men?" asked Babe.

"Rustlers," said Ma. "They'm sheep rustlers."

"What d'you mean?"

"Thieves, young un, that's what I do mean. Sheep stealers. We'll all be in that truck afore you can blink your eye."

"What can we do?"

"Do? Ain't nothing we can do, unless we can slip past this here wolf."

She made as if to escape, but the dog behind darted in, and she turned back.

Again, one of the men whistled, and the dog pressed. Gradually, held against the headland of the field by the second dog and the men, the flock began to move forward. Already the leaders were nearing the tailgate of the truck.

"We'm beat," said Ma mournfully. "You run for it, young un." I will, thought Babe, but not the way you mean. Little as he was, he felt suddenly not fear but anger, furious anger that the boss's sheep were being stolen. My mum's not here to protect them so I must, he said to himself bravely, and he ran quickly around the hedge side of the flock, and jumping onto the

Create a List

Journey a Log
Path to
Truck

Babe caught
All Lost / Then
Babe Rises

bottom of the tailgate, turned to face them.

"Please!" he cried. "I beg you! Please don't come any closer. If you would be so kind, dear sensible sheep!"

His unexpected appearance had a number of immediate effects. The shock of being so politely addressed stopped the flock in its tracks, and the cries of "Wolf!" changed to murmurs of "In't he lovely!" and "Proper little gennulman!" Ma had told them something of her new friend, and now to see him in the flesh and to hear his well-chosen words released them from the dominance of the dogs. They began to fidget and look about for an escape route. This was opened for them when the men (cursing quietly, for above all things they were anxious to avoid too much noise) sent the flanking dog to drive the pig away, and some of the sheep began to slip past them.

Next moment all was chaos. Angrily the dog ran at Babe, who scuttled away squealing at the top of his voice in a mixture of fright and fury. The men closed on him, sticks raised. Desperately he shot between the legs of one, who fell with a crash, while the other, striking out madly, hit the rearguard dog as it came to help, and sent it yowling. In half a minute the carefully planned raid was ruined, as the sheep scattered everywhere.

45

"Keep yelling, young un!" bawled Ma, as she ran beside Babe. "They won't never stay here with that row going on!"

And suddenly all sorts of things began to happen as those deafening squeals rang out over the quiet countryside. Birds flew startled from the trees, cows in nearby fields began to gallop about, dogs in distant farms to bark, passing motorists to stop and stare. In the farmhouse below Mrs. Hogget heard the noise as she had on the day of the Fair. She stuck her head out the window and saw the rustlers, their truck, galloping sheep, and Babe. She dialled 999 but then talked for so long that by the time a patrol car drove up the lane, the rustlers had long gone. Snarling at each other and their dogs, they had driven hurriedly away with not one single sheep to show for their pains.

"You won't never believe it!" cried Mrs. Hogget when her husband returned from market. "But we've had rustlers, just after you'd gone it were, come with a huge cattle truck they did, the police said, they seen the tire marks in the gateway, and a chap in a car seen the truck go by in a hurry, and there's been a lot of it about, and he give the alarm, he did, kept screaming and shrieking enough to bust your eardrums, we should have lost every sheep on the place if 'tweren't

47

for him, 'tis him we've got to thank."

"Who?" said Farmer Hogget.

"Him!" said his wife, pointing at Babe who was telling Fly all about it. "Don't ask me how he got there or why he done it, all I knows is he saved our bacon and now I'm going to save his, he's staying with us just like another dog, don't care if he gets as big as a house, because if you think I'm going to stand by and see him butchered after what he done for us today, you've got another think coming, what d'you say to that?"

A slow smile spread over Farmer Hogget's long face.

Mrs Hogget's Conversation — How does she know? Screaming. Babe Makes a Racket.

CHAPTER 6

"Good Pig"

The very next morning Farmer Hogget decided that he would see if the pig would like to come, when he went around the sheep with Fly. I'm daft, he thought, grinning to himself. He did not tell his wife.

Upon seeing him walk down the yard, crook in hand, and hearing him call Fly, Babe was about to settle down for an after-breakfast nap when to his surprise he heard the farmer's voice again.

"Come, Pig," said Farmer Hogget and to *his* surprise the pig came.

"I expect it's because of what you did yesterday," said Fly proudly, as they walked to heel together up the hill. "The boss must be very pleased with you, dear. You can watch me working."

When they reached the lower gate, Farmer Hogget opened it and left it open.

49

"He's going to bring them down into the home paddock, away from the lane," said Fly quickly. "You be quiet and keep out of the way," and she went to sit waiting by the farmer's right side.

"Come by!" he said, and Fly ran left up the slope as the sheep began to bunch above her. Once behind them, she addressed them in her usual way, that is to say, sharply.

"Move, fools!" she snapped. "Down the hill. If you know which way 'down' is," but to her surprise they did not obey. Instead they turned to face her, and some even stamped, and shook their heads at her, while a great chorus of bleating began.

50

"Good Pig"

To Fly sheep-talk was just so much rubbish, to which she had never paid any attention, but Babe, listening below, could hear clearly what was being said, and although the principal cry was the usual one, there were other voices saying other things. The contrast between the politeness with which they had been treated by yesterday's rescuer and the everlasting rudeness to which they were subjected by this or any wolf brought mutinous thoughts into woolly heads, and words of defiance rang out.

"You got no manners! . . . Why can't you ask nicely? . . . Treat us like muck, you do!" they cried, and one hoarse voice which the pig recognized called loudly, "We don't want you, wolf! We want Babe!" whereupon they all took it up.

"We want Babe!" they bleated. "Babe! Babe! Ba-a-a-a-a-be!"

Those behind pushed at those in front, so that they actually edged a pace or two nearer the dog.

For a moment it seemed to Babe that Fly was not going to be able to move them, that she would lose this particular battle of wills; but he had not reckoned with her years of experience. Suddenly, quick as a flash, she drove in on them with a growl and with a twisting leap sprang for the nose of the foremost animal; Babe heard the clack of her teeth as the ewe

51

Fly
fights
Back

Against
the
Mutiny

fell over backward in fright, a fright which immediately ran through all. Defiant no longer, the flock poured down the hill, Fly snapping furiously at their heels, and surged wildly through the gateway.

"No manners! No manners! No ma-a-a-a-a-a-nners!" they cried, but an air of panic ran through them as they realized how rebellious they had been. How the wolf would punish them! They ran helter-skelter into the middle of the paddock, and wheeled as one to look back, ears pricked, eyes wide with fear. They puffed and blew, and Ma's hacking cough rang out. But to their surprise they saw that the wolf had dropped by the gateway, and that after a moment the pig came trotting out to one side of them.

Though Farmer Hogget could not know what had caused the near-revolt of the flock, he saw clearly that for some reason they had given Fly a hard time, and that she was angry. It was not like her to gallop sheep in that pell-mell fashion.

"Steady!" he said curtly as she harried the rear-guard, and then "Down!" and "Stay!" and shut the gate. Shepherding suited Farmer Hogget—there was no waste of words in it.

In the corner of the home paddock closest to the farm buildings was a smallish fenced yard divided

into a number of pens and runways. Here the sheep would be brought at shearing time or to pick out fat lambs for market or to be treated for various troubles. Farmer Hogget had heard the old ewe cough; he thought he would catch her up and give her another potion. He turned to give an order to Fly lying flat and still behind him, and there, lying flat and still beside her, was the pig.

"Stay, Fly!" said Hogget. And, just for fun, "Come, Pig!"

Immediately Babe ran forward and sat at the farmer's right, his front trotters placed neatly together, his big ears cocked for the next command.

Strange thoughts began to stir in Farmer Hogget's mind, and unconsciously he crossed his fingers.

He took a deep breath, and, holding it . . . "Away to me, Pig!" he said softly.

Without a moment's hesitation Babe began the long outrun to the right.

Quite what Farmer Hogget had expected to happen, he could never afterwards clearly remember. What he had not expected was that the pig would run round to the rear of the flock, and turn to face it and him, and lie down instantly without a word of further command spoken, just as a well-trained dog would have done. Admittedly, with his jerky little rocking-

54

horse canter he took twice as long to get there as Fly
would have, but still, there he was, in the right place,
ready and waiting. Admittedly, the sheep had turned
to face the pig and were making a great deal of noise,
but then Farmer Hogget did not know, and Fly
would not listen to, what they were saying. He called
the dog to heel, and began to walk with his long
loping stride to the collecting pen in the corner. Out
in the middle of the paddock there was quite a babble
of talk.

55

"Good morning!" said Babe. "I do hope I find you all well, and not too distressed by yesterday's experience?" and immediately it seemed that every sheep had something to say to him.

"Bless his heart!" they cried, and, "Dear little soul!" and, "Hullo, Babe!" and, "Nice to see you again!" and then there was a rasping cough and the sound of Ma's hoarse tones.

"What's up then, young un?" she croaked. "What be you doing here instead of that wolf?"

Although Babe wanted, literally, to keep on the right side of the sheep, his loyalty to his foster mother made him say in a rather hurt voice, "She's not a wolf. She's a sheepdog."

"Oh all right then," said Ma, "sheepdog, if you must have it. What do you want, then?"

Babe looked at the army of long sad faces.

"I want to be a sheep-pig," he said.

"Ha ha!" bleated a big lamb standing next to Ma. "Ha ha ha-a-a-a-a!"

"Be quiet!" said Ma sharply, swinging her head to give the lamb a thumping butt in the side. "That ain't nothing to laugh at."

Raising her voice, she addressed the flock.

"Listen to me, all you ewes," she said, "and lambs too. This young chap was kind to me, like I told you,

Sheep's Rights
Dignity —
Sheep Have You
claim

Dignity

Have you
Assert

Your
Dignity

when I were poorly. And I told him, if he was to ask me to go somewhere or do something, politely, like he would, why, I'd be only too delighted. We ain't stupid, I told him, all we do want is to be treated right, and we'm as bright as the next beast, we are."

"We are!" chorused the flock. "We are! We are! We a-a-a-a-a-are!"

"Right then," said Ma. "What shall us do, Babe?"

Babe looked across toward Farmer Hogget, who had opened the gate of the collecting pen and now stood leaning on his crook, Fly at his feet. The pen was in the left bottom corner of the paddock, and so Babe expected, and at that moment got, the command "Come by, Pig!" to send him left and so behind the sheep and thus turn them down toward the corner.

He cleared his throat. "If I might ask a great favor of you," he said hurriedly, "could you all please be kind enough to walk down to that gate where the farmer is standing, and to go through it? Take your time, please, there's absolutely no rush."

A look of pure contentment passed over the faces of the flock, and almost as one they turned and walked across the paddock, Babe a few paces in their rear. They walked sedately and steadily, over to the corner, through the gate, into the pen, and then stood

the Joy of Respect

57

quietly waiting. No one broke rank or tried to slip away, no one pushed or shoved, there was no noise or fuss. From the oldest to the youngest, they went in like lambs.

Then, at last, a gentle murmur broke out as everyone in different ways quietly expressed their pleasure.

"Babe!" said Fly to the pig. "That was quite beautifully done, dear!"

"Thank you so much!" said Babe to the sheep. "You did that so nicely!"

"Ta!" said the sheep. "Ta! Ta! Ta-a-a-a-a-a! 'Tis a pleasure to work for such a little gennulman!" And Ma added, "You'll make a wunnerful sheep-pig, young un, or my name's not Ma-a-a-a-a-a."

As for Farmer Hogget, he heard none of this, so wrapped up was he in his own thoughts. He's as good as a dog, he told himself excitedly, he's better than a dog, than any dog! I wonder . . . !

"Good Pig," he said.

Then he uncrossed his fingers and closed the gate.

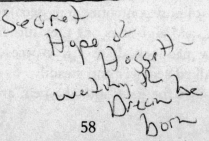

Secret
Hope of
Hogett —
welthy the
Dream be
born

58

CHAPTER 7

"What's trials?"

Every day after that, of course, Babe went the rounds with Farmer Hogget and Fly. At first the farmer worried about using the pig to herd the sheep, not because it was a strange and unusual thing to do which people might laugh at—he did not care about that—but because he was afraid it might upset Fly and put her nose out of joint. However it did not seem to do so.

He could have spared himself the worry if he had been able to listen to their conversation.

"That *was* fun!" said Babe to Fly that evening. "I wonder if the boss will let me do some more work?"

"I'm sure he will, dear. You did it so well. It was almost as though the sheep knew exactly what it was you wanted them to do."

"But that's just it! I asked them . . ."

Struggle over how to accomplish
Goals — Fly vs Babe

"No use *asking* sheep anything, dear," interrupted Fly. "You have to *make* them do what you want, I've told you before."

"Yes, Mum. But . . . will you mind, if the boss uses me instead of you, sometimes?"

"Mind?" said Fly. "You bet your trotters I won't! All my life I've had to run around after those idiots, up hill, down dale, day in, day out. And as for 'sometimes,' as far as I'm concerned you can work them every day. I'm not as young as I was. I'll be only too happy to lie comfortably in the grass and watch you, my Babe."

And before long that was exactly what she was doing. Once Farmer Hogget could see by her wagging tail and smiling eyes that she was perfectly happy about it, he began to use Babe to do some of her work. At first he only gave the pig simple tasks,

but as the days and weeks went by, Hogget began to make more and more use of his new helper. The speed with which Babe learned amazed him, and before long he was relying on him for all the work with the flock, while Fly lay and proudly watched. Now, there was nothing, it seemed, that the pig could not do, and do faultlessly, at that.

He obeyed all the usual commands immediately and correctly. He could fetch sheep or take them away, move them to left or right, persuade them to move around obstacles or through gaps, cut the flock in half, or take out one individual.

To work on Ma, for instance, there was no need for Hogget to bring all the sheep down to the collecting pen, or to corner them all and catch her by a hind leg with his crook. He could simply point her out to the pig, and Babe would gently work her out of the bunch and bring her right to the farmer's feet, where she stood quietly waiting. It seemed like a miracle to Hogget, but of course it was simple.

"Ma!"

"Yes, young un?"

"The boss wants to give you some more medicine."

"Oh not again! 'Tis horrible stuff, that."

"But it'll make your cough better."

"Oh ar?"

"Come along, Ma. Please."

"Oh all right then, young un. Anything to oblige you."

And there were other far more miraculous things that Babe could easily have done if the farmer had only known. For example, when it was time for the ewes to be separated from their lambs, now almost as big and strong as their mothers, Farmer Hogget behaved like any other shepherd, and brought the whole flock down to the pens, and took a lot of time and trouble to part them. If only he had been able to explain things to Babe, how easy it could have been.

"Dear ladies, will you please stay on the hill, if you'd be so kind?"

"Youngsters, down you go to the collecting pen if you please, there's good boys and girls," and it could have been done in the shake of a lamb's tail.

However, Babe's increasing skill at working sheep made Farmer Hogget determined to take the next step in a plan which had begun to form in his mind on the day the piglet had first penned the sheep. That step was nothing less than to take Pig with him to the local sheepdog trials in a couple of weeks' time. Only just to watch of course, just so that he could have a look at well-trained dogs working a small number of sheep, and see what they and their handlers were required to do. I'm daft, he thought, grinning to himself. He did not tell his wife.

Before the day came, he put a collar and lead on the pig. He could not risk him running away, in a strange place. He kept him on the lead all one morning, letting Fly do the work as of old. He need not have bothered—Babe would have stayed tight at heel when told—but it was interesting to note the instant change in the atmosphere as the collie ran out.

"Wolf! Wolf!" cried the flock, every sheep immediately on edge.

"Move, fools!" snapped Fly, and she hustled them and bustled them with little regard for their feelings.

"Babe! We want Babe!" they bleated. "Ba–a–a–a–a–a–be!"

To be sure, the work was done more quickly, but at the end of it the sheep were scared and trembling and the dog out of patience and breath.

"Steady! Steady!" called the farmer a number of times, something he never had to say to Babe.

When the day came for the local trials, Farmer Hogget set off early in the Land Rover, Fly and Babe in the back. He told his wife where he was going, though not that he was taking the pig. Nor did he say that he did not intend to be an ordinary spectator, but instead more of a spy, to see without being seen. He wanted Pig to observe everything that went on without being spotted. Now that he had settled on the final daring part of his plan, Hogget realized that secrecy was all-important. No one must know that he owned a . . . what would you call him, he thought . . . a sheep-pig, I suppose!

The trials took place ten miles or so away, in a curved basin-shaped valley in the hills. At the lower end of the basin was a road. Close to this was the starting point, where the dogs would begin their outrun, and also the enclosure where they would finally pen their sheep. Down there all the spectators would gather. Farmer Hogget, arriving some time before them, parked the Land Rover in a lane, and set off up the valley by a roundabout way, keeping in the shelter of the bordering woods, Fly padding behind him and Babe on the lead trotting to keep up with his long strides.

"Where are we going, Mum?" said Babe excitedly. "What are we going to do?"

"I don't think we're going to do anything, dear," said Fly. "I think the boss wants you to see something."

"What?"

They had reached the head of the valley now, and the farmer found a suitable place to stop, under cover, but with a good view of the course.

"Down, Fly, down, Pig, and stay," he said and exhausted by this long speech, stretched his long frame on the ground and settled down to wait.

"Wants me to see what?" said Babe.

"The trials."

"What's trials?"

"Well," said Fly, "it's a sort of competition, for

sheepdogs and their bosses. Each dog has to fetch five sheep, and move them through a number of gaps and gateways—you can see which ones, they've got flags on either side—down to that circle that's marked out in the field right at the bottom, and there the dog has to shed some sheep."

"What's 'shed' mean?"

"Separate them out from the rest; the ones to be shed will have collars on."

"And then what?"

"Then the dog has to gather them all again, and pen them."

"Is that all?"

"It's not easy, dear. Not like moving that bunch of woolly fools of ours up and down a field. It all has to be done quickly, without any mistakes. You lose points if you make mistakes."

"Have you ever been in a trial, Mum?"

"Yes. Here. When I was younger."

"Did you make any mistakes?"

"Of course," said Fly. "Everyone does. It's very difficult, working a small number of strange sheep, in strange country. You'll see."

By the end of the day Babe had seen a great deal. The course was not an easy one, and the sheep were

67

very different from those at home. They were fast
and wild, and, good though the dogs were, there
were many mistakes made, at the gates, in the
shedding ring, at the final penning.

Babe watched every run intently, and Hogget
watched Babe, and Fly watched them both.

What's the boss up to, she thought, as they drove
home. He's surely never thinking that one day Babe
might . . . no, he couldn't be that daft! Sheep-pig
indeed! All right for the little chap to run round our
place for a bit of fun, but to think of him competing

68

in trials, even a little local one like today's, well, really! She remembered something Babe had said in his early duck-herding days.

"I suppose you'd say," she remarked now, "that those dogs just weren't polite enough?"

"That's right," said Babe.

CHAPTER 8

"Oh Ma!"

Fly's suspicions about what the farmer was up to grew rapidly over the next weeks. It soon became obvious to her that he was constructing, on his own land, a practice course. From the top of the field where the rustlers had come, the circuit which he laid out ran all around the farm, studded with hazards to be negotiated. Some were existing gateways or gaps. Some he made, with hurdles, or lines of posts between which the sheep had to be driven. Some were extremely difficult. One, for example, a plank bridge over a stream, was so narrow that it could only be crossed in single file, and the most honeyed words were needed from Babe to persuade the animals to cross.

Then, in the home paddock, Hogget made a rough shedding ring with a circle of large stones, and

70

beyond it, a final pen, a small hurdle enclosure no bigger than a tiny room, with a gate which was to close when he pulled on a rope.

Every day the farmer would send Fly to cut out five sheep from the flock, and take them to the top of the hill, and hold them there. Then, starting Babe from the gate at the lower end of the farmyard, Hogget would send him away to run them through the course.

"Away to me, Pig!" he would say, or "Come by, Pig!" and off Babe would scamper as fast as his trotters could carry him, as the farmer pulled out his big old pocket watch and noted the time. There was only one problem. His trotters wouldn't carry him all that fast.

Here at home, Fly realized, his lack of speed didn't matter much. Whichever five sheep were selected were only too anxious to oblige Babe, and would hurry eagerly to do whatever he wanted. But with strange sheep it will be different, thought Fly. If the boss really does intend to run him in a trial. Which it looks as if he does! She watched Babe's tubby pinky-white shape as he crested the hill.

That evening at suppertime she watched again as he tucked into his food. Up till now it had never worried her how much he ate. He's a growing boy, she had

thought fondly. Now she thought, he's a greedy boy too.

"Babe," she said, as with a grunt of content he licked the last morsels off the end of his snout. His little tin trough was as shiningly clean as though Mrs. Hogget had washed it in her sink, and his tummy was as tight as a drum.

"Yes, Mum?"

"You like being a . . . sheep-pig, don't you?"

"Oh yes, Mum!"

"And you'd like to be really good at it, wouldn't you? The greatest? Better than any other sheep-pig?"

"D'you think there are any others?"

"Well, no. Better than any sheepdog, then?"

"Oh yes, I'd love to be! But I don't really think that's possible. You see, although sheep do seem to behave well for me, and do what I ask . . . I mean, do what I *tell* them, I'm nowhere near as fast as a dog and never will be."

"No. But you could be a jolly sight faster than you are."

"How?"

"Well, there are two things you'd have to do, dear. First, you'd have to go into proper training. One little run around a day's not enough. You'd have to practice hard—jogging, cross-crountry running, sprinting, distance work. I'd help you of course."

It all sounded like fun to Babe.

"Great!" he said. "But you said 'two things.' What's the second?"

"Eat less," said Fly. "You'd have to go on a diet."

Any ordinary pig would have rebelled at this point. Pigs enjoy eating, and they also enjoy lying around

73

most of the day thinking about eating again. But Babe was no ordinary pig, and he set out enthusiastically to do what Fly suggested.

Under her watchful eye he ate wisely but not too well, and every afternoon he trained, to a program which she had worked out, trotting right around the boundaries of the farm perhaps, or running up to the top of the hill and back again, or racing up and down the home paddock. Hogget thought that Pig was just playing, but he couldn't help noticing how he had grown; not fatter, as a sty-kept pig would have done, but stronger and more wiry. There was nothing of the piglet about him anymore; he looked lean and racy and hard-muscled, and he was now almost as big as the sheep he herded. And the day came when that strength and hardness were to stand him in good stead.

One beautiful morning, when the sky was clear and cloudless, and the air so crisp and fresh that you could almost taste it, Babe woke feeling on top of the world. Like a trained athlete, he felt so charged with energy that he simply couldn't keep still. He bounced about the stable floor on all four feet, shaking his head about and uttering a series of short sharp squeaks.

"You're full of it this morning," said Fly with a

74

yawn. "You'd better run to the top of the hill and back to work it off."

"O.K. Mum!" said Babe, and off he shot while Fly settled comfortably back in the straw.

Dashing across the home paddock, Babe bounded up the hill and looked about for the sheep. Though he knew he would see them later on, he felt so pleased with life that he thought he would like to share that feeling with Ma and all the others, before he ran home again; just to say "Hello! Good morning, everybody! Isn't it a lovely day!" They were, he knew, in the most distant of all the fields on the farm, up at the top of the lane.

He looked across, expecting that they would be grazing quietly or lying comfortably and cudding in the morning sun, only to see them galloping madly in every direction. On the breeze came cries of "Wolf!" but not in the usual bored, almost automatic tones of complaint that they used when Fly worked them. These were yells of real terror, desperate calls for help. As he watched, two other animals came in sight, one large, one small, and he heard the sound of barking and yapping as they dashed about after the fleeing sheep. "You get some wolves as'll chase sheep and kill 'em"—Ma's exact words came back to Babe, and without a second thought he set off as fast as he could go in the direction of the noise.

What a sight greeted him when he arrived in the far field! The flock, usually so tightly bunched, was scattered everywhere, eyes bulging, mouths open, heads hanging in their evident distress, and it was clear that the dogs had been at their worrying for some time. A few sheep had tried in their terror to jump the wire fencing and had become caught up in it, some had fallen into the ditches and got stuck. Some were limping as they ran about, and on the grass were lumps of wool torn from others.

Most dreadful of all, in the middle of the field, the worriers had brought down a ewe, which lay on its side, feebly kicking at them as they growled and tugged at it.

"Oh Ma!"

On the day when the rustlers had come, Babe had felt a mixture of fear and anger. Now he knew nothing but a blind rage, and he charged flat out at the two dogs, grunting and snorting with fury. Nearest to him was the smaller dog, a kind of mongrel terrier, which was snapping at one of the ewe's hind legs, deaf to everything in the excitement of the worry.

Before it could move, Babe took it across the back and flung it to one side, and the force of his rush carried him on into the bigger dog and knocked it flying.

This one, a large black crossbreed, part-collie, part-retriever, was made of sterner stuff than the terrier, which was already running dazedly away; and it picked itself up and came snarling back at the pig. Perhaps, in the confusion of the moment, it thought that this was just another sheep that had somehow

found courage to attack it; but if so, it soon knew better, for as it came on, Babe chopped at it with his terrible pig's bite, the bite that grips and tears, and now it was not sheep's blood that was spilled.

Howling in pain, the black dog turned and ran, his tail between his legs. He ran, in fact, for his life, an openmouthed bristling pig hard on his heels.

The field was clear, and Babe suddenly came back to his senses. He turned and hurried to the fallen ewe, round whom, now that the dogs had gone, the horrified flock was beginning to gather in a rough circle. She lay still now, as Babe stood panting by her side, a draggled side where the worriers had pulled at it, and suddenly he realized. It was Ma!

"Ma!" he cried. "Ma! Are you all right?"

She did not seem too badly hurt. He could not see any gaping wounds, though blood was coming from one ear where the dogs had bitten it.

The old ewe opened an eye. Her voice, when she spoke, was as hoarse as ever, but now not much more than a whisper.

"Hullo, young un," she said.

Babe dropped his head and gently licked the ear to try to stop the bleeding, and some blood stuck to his snout.

"Can you get up?" he asked.

78

"Oh Ma!"

For some time Ma did not answer, and he looked anxiously at her, but the eye that he could see was still open.

"I don't reckon," she said.

"It's all right, Ma," Babe said. "The wolves have gone, far away."

"Far, far, fa-a-a-a-a-ar!" chorused the flock.

"And Fly and the boss will soon be here to look after you."

Ma made no answer or movement. Only her ribs jumped to the thump of her tired old heart.

"You'll be all right, honestly you will," said Babe.

"Oh ar," said Ma, and then the eye closed and the ribs jumped no more.

"Oh Ma!" said Babe, and "Ma! Ma! Ma-a-a-a-a-a!" mourned the flock, as the Land Rover came up the lane.

Farmer Hogget had heard nothing of the worrying —the field was too far away, the wind in the wrong direction—but he had been anxious, and so by now was Fly, because Pig was nowhere to be found.

The moment they entered the field both man and dog could see that something was terribly wrong. Why else was the flock so obviously distressed, panting and gasping and disheveled? Why had they formed that ragged circle, and what was in the middle of it? Farmer Hogget strode forward, Fly before him parting the ring to make way, only to see a sight that struck horror into the hearts of both.

There before them lay a dead ewe, and bending over it was the pig, his snout almost touching the outstretched neck, a snout, they saw, that was stained with blood.

CHAPTER 9

"Was it Babe?"

"Go home, Pig!" said Farmer Hogget in a voice that was so quiet and cold that Babe hardly recognized it. Bewildered, he trotted off obediently, while behind him the farmer picked up the dead ewe and carried it to the Land Rover. Then with Fly's help he began the task of rescuing those sheep that were caught or stuck, and of making sure that no others were badly hurt. This done, he left Fly to guard the flock, and drove home.

Back at the farm, Babe felt simply very very sad. The sky was still cloudless, the air still crisp, but this was a very different pig from the one that had cantered carefree up the hill not half an hour ago. In those thirty minutes he had seen naked fear and cruelty and death, and now to cap it all, the boss was angry with

him, had sent him home in some sort of disgrace.
What had he done wrong? He had only done his duty,
as a good sheep–pig should. He sat in the doorway of
the stables and watched as the Land Rover drove into
the yard, poor Ma's head lolling loosely over the
back. He saw the boss get out and go into the house,
and then, a few minutes later, come out again,
carrying something in the crook of one arm, a long
thing, a kind of black shiny tube, and walk toward
him.

"Come, Pig," said Farmer Hogget in that same
cold voice, and strode past him into the stables, while
at the same moment, inside the farmhouse, the
telephone began to ring, and then stopped as Mrs.
Hogget picked it up.

Obediently Babe followed the farmer into the dark
interior. It was not so dark however that he could not
see clearly that the boss was pointing the black shiny
tube at him, and he sat down again and waited,
supposing that perhaps it was some machine for
giving out food and that some quite unexpected
surprise would come out of its two small round
mouths, held now quite close to his face.

At that instant Mrs. Hogget's voice sounded across
the yard, calling her husband's name from the open
kitchen window. He frowned, lowered the shiny

tube, and poked his head around the stable door.

"Oh there you are!" called Mrs. Hogget. "What do you think, that was the police that was, they'm ringing every farmer in the district to warn 'em, there's sheep-worrying dogs about, they killed six sheep t'other side of the valley only last night, they bin seen they have, two of 'em 'tis, a big black un and a little brown un, they say to shoot 'em on sight if you do see 'em, you better get back up the hill and make sure ours is all right, d'you want me to fetch your gun?"

"No," said Farmer Hogget. "It's all right," he said.

He waited till his wife had shut the window and disappeared, and then he walked out into the sunlight with Babe following.

"Sit, Pig," he said, but now his voice was warm and friendly again.

He looked closely at the trusting face turned up to his, and saw, sticking to the side of Babe's mouth, some hairs, some black hairs, and a few brown ones too.

He shook his head in wonder, and that slow grin spread over his face.

"I reckon you gave them summat to worry about," he said, and he opened the gun and took out the cartridges.

Meanwhile Fly, standing guard up in the far field, was terribly agitated. She knew of course that some dogs will attack sheep, sometimes even the very dogs trained to look after them, but surely not her sheep-pig? Surely Babe could not have done such a thing? Yet there he had been at the center of that scene of chaos, bloodstained and standing over a dead ewe! What would the boss do to him, what perhaps had he already done? Yet she could not leave these fools to find out.

At least though, she suddenly realized, they could tell her what had happened, if the shock hadn't driven what little sense they had out of their stupid heads. Never before in her long life had Fly sunk to engaging a sheep in conversation. They were there to be ordered about, like soldiers, and, like soldiers, never to answer back. She approached the nearest one, with distaste, and it promptly backed away from her.

"Stand still, fool!" she barked. "And tell me who chased you. Who killed that old one?"

"Wolf," said the sheep automatically.

Fly growled with annoyance. Was that the only word the halfwits knew? She put the question differently.

"Was it the pig that chased you? Was it Babe?" she said.

"Ba-a-a-a-abe!" bleated the sheep eagerly.

"What does that mean, bonehead?" barked Fly. "Was it or wasn't it?"

"Wolf," said the sheep.

Somehow Fly controlled her anger at the creature's stupidity. I *must* know what happened, she thought. Babe's always talking about being polite to these woolly idiots. I'll have to try it. I must know. She took a deep breath.

"Please . . ." she said. The sheep, which had begun to graze, raised its head sharply and stared at her with an expression of total amazement.

"Say that agai-ai-ai-ain," it said, and a number of others, overhearing, moved toward the collie.

"Please," said Fly, swallowing hard, "could you be kind enough to tell me . . ."

"Hark!" interrupted the first sheep. "Hark! Ha-a-a-a-ark!" whereupon the whole flock ran and gathered round. They stood in silence, every eye fixed wonderingly on her, every mouth hanging open. Nincompoops! thought Fly. Just when I wanted to ask one quietly the whole fatheaded lot come round. But I must know. I must know the truth about my Babe, however terrible it is.

"Please," she said once more in a voice choked with the effort of being humble, "could you be kind enough to tell me what happened this morning? Did Babe . . . ?" but she got no further, for at the mention of the pig's name the whole flock burst out into a great cry of "Ba-a-a-a-abe!"

Listening, for the first time ever, to what the sheep were actually saying, Fly could hear individual voices competing to make themselves heard, in what was nothing less than a hymn of praise. "Babe ca-a-a-a-ame!" "He sa-a-a-a-aved us!" "He drove the wolves

86

awa-a-a-a-ay!" "He made them pa-a-a-a-ay!" "Hip
hip hooray! Hip hip hooray! Hip hip hoora-a-a-ay!"

What a sense of relief flooded over her as she heard
and understood the words of the sheep! It had been
sheep-worriers, after all! And her boy had come to
the rescue! He was not the villain, he was the hero!

Hogget and Babe heard the racket as they climbed the
hill, and the farmer sent the pig ahead, fearing that
perhaps the worriers had returned.

Under cover of the noise Babe arrived on the scene
unnoticed by Fly, just in time to hear her reply.

"Oh thank you!" she cried to the flock. "Thank
you all so much for telling me! How kind of you!"

"Gosh, Mum," said a voice behind her. "What's
come over you?"

87

CHAPTER 10

"Memorize it"

Because Babe had now saved the flock not only from rustlers but also from the worriers, the Hoggets could not do too much for him.

Because he was a pig (though Farmer Hogget increasingly found himself thinking of Pig as Dog and fed him accordingly), they gave him unlimited supplies of what they supposed he could not have too much of—namely, food.

Because he was strong-minded and reveled in his newfound speed, he ate sparingly of it.

Because there was always a lot left over, Fly became fat and the chickens chubby and the ducks dumpy, and the very rats and mice rolled happily about the stables with stomachs full to bursting.

Mrs. Hogget even took to calling Babe to the back door, to feed him some tidbit or other that she

88

thought he might particularly like; and from here it was but a short step to inviting him into the house, which one day she did.

When the farmer came in for his tea, he found not only Fly but also Pig lying happily asleep beside the old stove. And afterward, when he sat down in his armchair in the sitting room and switched on the television, Babe came to sit beside him, and they watched the six o'clock news together.

"He likes it," said Hogget to his wife when she came into the room. Mrs. Hogget nodded her head a great many times, and as usual had a few words to say on the subject.

"Dear little chap, though you can't call him little no longer, he's growed so much, why, he's big enough to you-know-what, not that we ever shall now, over my dead body though I hopes it ain't if you see what I do mean, just look at him, we should have brought him in the house long ago, no reason why not, is there now?"

"He might mess the carpet," said Farmer Hogget.

"Never!" cried Mrs. Hogget, shaking her head the entire time that she was speaking. "He's no more likely to mess than he is to fly, he'll ask to go out when he wants to do his do's, just like a good clean dog would, got more brains than a dog he has, why 'twouldn't surprise me to hear he was rounding up them old sheep of yourn, 'twouldn't honestly, though I suppose you think I'm daft?"

Farmer Hogget grinned to himself. He did not tell his wife what she had never yet noticed, that all the work of the farm was now done by the sheep-pig. And he had no intention of telling her of the final part of his plan, which was nothing less than to enter Pig in that sternest of all tests, the Grand Challenge Sheep Dog Trials, open to all comers! Never in his working life had he owned an animal good enough to compete in these trials. Now at last he had one, and he was not going to be stopped from realizing his ambition by the fact that it was a pig.

In a couple of weeks they would be competing against the best sheepdogs in the country, would be appearing, in fact, on that very television screen they were now watching.

"No, you're not daft," he said.

But you won't get half a surprise when you sit here and watch it he thought. And so will a lot of other folks.

His plan was simple. He would appear at the Grand Challenge Trials with Fly, and at the last possible moment swap her for Pig. By then it would be too late for anyone to stop him. It didn't matter what

Bildy exchnt

happened afterwards—they could disqualify him,
fine him, send him to prison, anything—as long as he
could run Pig, just one glorious run, just to show
them all!

And they couldn't say they hadn't been warned
—the name was there on the entry form. He had been
worried, for he was a truthful man, that the heading
might say 'Name of Dog,' and then whatever he put
would be a lie. But he'd been lucky. "Name of
Competitor" (the form said) . . . "F. Hogget."
"Name of Entry" . . . "Pig."

The simple truth.

Shepherds usually give their dogs short names, like
Gyp or Moss—it's so much quicker and easier than
shouting "Bartholomew!" or "Wilhelmina!"—and
though someone might say "'Pig'? That's a funny
name," no one in their wildest dreams would guess
that was the simple truth.

The two weeks before the Grand Challenge Trials
were two weeks of concentrated activity. Apart from
Mrs. Hogget who as usual was busy with household
duties, everyone now knew what was going on. To
begin with, Hogget altered the practice course, cut-
ting out all the frills like the plank bridge over the
stream, and he built a new course as close as possible

to what he thought they might face on the day.

As soon as Fly saw this, she became convinced that what she had suspected was actually going to happen, and she told the sheep, with whom she was now on speaking terms.

Every night of course she and Babe talked endlessly about the coming challenge before they settled to sleep (in the stables still, though the Hoggets would have been perfectly happy for Babe to sleep in the house, so well-mannered was he).

93

Thoughtful as ever, Babe was anxious, not about his own abilities but about his foster mother's feelings. He felt certain she would have given her dog teeth to compete in the National Trials, the dream of every sheepdog, yet she must sit and watch him.

"Are you *sure* you don't mind, Mum?" he asked.

Fly's reply was as practical as ever.

"Listen, Babe," she said. "First of all it wouldn't matter whether I minded or not. The boss is going to run you, no doubt of it. Second, I'm too old and too fat, and anyway I was only ever good enough for small local competitions. And lastly, I'll be the happiest collie in the world if you win. And you can win."

"D'you really think so?"

"I'm sure of it," said Fly firmly, but all the same she was anxious too—about one thing.

She knew that the sheep-pig, speedy as he now was, would still be much slower than the dogs, especially on the outrun; but equally she was confident that he could make this up by the promptness with which the sheep obeyed his requests. Here, at home, they shot through gaps or around obstacles as quick as a flash, never putting a foot wrong; the ones to be shed dashed out of the ring like lightning; and at the final penning, they popped in the instant that the boss opened the gate. But that was here, at home. What would strange sheep do? How would they react to Babe? Would he be able to communicate with them, in time, for there would be none to waste?

She determined to ask the flock, and one evening when Babe and the boss were watching television, she trotted off up the hill. Since that first time when she had been forced to speak civilly to them, they no longer cried "Wolf!" at her, and now they gathered around attentively at her first words, words that were carefully polite.

"Good evening," said Fly. "I wonder if you would be kind enough to help me? I've a little problem," and she explained it, speaking slowly and carefully (for sheep are stupid, she said to herself, nobody will ever persuade me otherwise).

"You see what I mean?" she finished. "There they'll be, these strange sheep, and I'm sure they'll do what he tells them . . . asks them, I mean . . . eventually, but it'll all take time, explaining things. The last creature they'll be expecting to see is a pig, and they might just bolt at the sight of him, before he even gets a chance to speak to them."

"Password," said several voices.

"What do you mean?" Fly said.

"Password, password, Pa-a-a-a-assword!" said

95

many voices now, speaking slowly and carefully (for wolves are stupid, they said to themselves, nobody will ever persuade us otherwise).

"What our Babe's got to do," said one, "is to larn what all of us larned when we was little lambs."

"'Tis a saying, see," said another, "as lambs do larn at their mothers' hocks."

"And then wherever we do go . . ."

". . . to ma–a–a–arket . . ."

". . . or to another fa–a–a–arm . . ."

". . . we won't never come to no ha–a–a–arm . . ."

". . . so long as we do say the pa–a–assword!"

"And if our Babe do say it to them . . ."

". . . why then, they won't never run away!"

Fly felt her patience slipping, but she controlled herself, knowing how important this information could be.

"Please," she said quietly, "please will you tell me the password?"

For a long moment the flock stood silent, the only movement a turning of heads as they looked at one another. Fly could sense that they were braving themselves to tell this age-old secret, to give away —to a wolf, of all things—this treasured countersign.

Then "'Tis for Babe," someone said, "'tis for his sa–a–a–ake."

"Ah!" they all said softly. "A-a-a-a-a-a-ah!" and then with one voice they began to intone:

"I may be ewe, I may be ram,
I may be mutton, may be lamb,
But on the hoof or on the hook,
I bain't so stupid as I look."

Then by general consent they began to move away, grazing as they went.

"Is that it?" called Fly after them. "Is that the password?" and the murmur came back "A-a-a-a-a-a-a-a-a-ar!"

"But what does it all mean, Mum?" said Babe that night when she told him. "All that stuff about 'I may be you' and other words I don't understand. It doesn't make sense to me."

"That doesn't matter, dear," said Fly. "You just memorize it. It may make all the difference on the day."

CHAPTER 11

"Today is the day"

The day, when it dawned, was just that little bit too bright.

On the opposite side of the valley the trees and houses and haystacks stood out clearly against the background in that three-dimensional way that means rain later.

Farmer Hogget came out and sniffed the air and looked around. Then he went inside again to fetch waterproof clothing.

Fly knew, the moment that she set eyes on the boss, that this was the day. Dogs have lived so long with humans that they know what's going to happen, sometimes even before their owners do. She woke Babe.

"Today," she said.

"Today what, Mum?" said Babe sleepily.

"Today is the day of the Grand Challenge Sheep-

98

dog Trials," said Fly proudly. "Which you, dear," she added in a confident voice, "are going to win!" With a bit of luck, she thought, and tenderly she licked the end of his snout.

She looked critically at the rest of him, anxious as any mother that her child should look right if he is to appear in public.

"Oh Babe!" she said. "Your coat's in an awful mess. What have you been doing with yourself? You look just as though you've been wallowing in the duck pond."

"Yes."

"You mean you have?"

"Yes, Mum."

Fly was on the point of saying that puppies don't do such things, when she remembered that he was, after all, a pig.

"Well, I don't know about Large *White*," she said. "You've certainly grown enormous but it's anyone's guess what color you are under all that muck. Whatever's to be done?"

Immediately her question was answered.

"Come, Pig," said Hogget's voice from the yard, and when they came out of the stables, there stood the farmer with hosepipe and scrubbing brush and pails of soapy water.

Half an hour later, when a beautifully clean shining
Babe stood happily dripping while Hogget brushed
out the tassle of his tight-curled tail till it looked like
candy floss, Mrs. Hogget stuck her head out of the
kitchen window.

"Breakfast's ready," she called, "but what in the
world you doing with that pig, taking him to a pig
show or summat, I thought you was going to drive
up and watch the trials today, anybody'd think you
was going to enter 'e in them the way you've got un
done up, only he wouldn't be a sheepdog, he'd be a
sheep-pig wouldn't 'e, tee hee, whoever heard of such
a thing, I must be daft though it's you that's daft
really, carrying him about in the poor old Land Rover
the size he is now, the bottom'll fall out, I shouldn't
wonder, you ain't surely going to drive all that way
with him in the back just so's he can watch?"

"No," said Farmer Hogget.

Mrs. Hogget considered this answer for a moment
with her mouth open, while raising and lowering her
eyebrows, shaking her head, and drumming on the
windowsill with her fingertips. Then she closed her
mouth and the window.

After breakfast she came out to see them off. Fly was
sitting in the passenger seat, Babe was comfortable in

100

a thick bed of clean straw in the back, where he now took up the whole space.

Mrs. Hogget walked around the Land Rover, giving out farewells pats.

"Good boy," she said to Babe, and "Good girl," to Fly. And to Hogget, "Goodbye and have you got your sandwiches and your thermos of coffee and your raincoat, looks as if it might rain, thought I felt a spot just now though I suppose it might be different where you'm going seeing as it's a hundred miles away, that reminds me have you got enough gas or if not enough money to get some if you haven't if you do see what I do mean, drive carefully, see you later."

"Two o'clock," said Hogget. And before his wife had time to say anything, added, "On the telly. Live," and put the Land Rover into gear and drove away.

When Mrs. Hogget switched the television on at two o'clock, the first thing in the picture that she noticed was that it was raining hard. She dashed outside to bring her washing in, saw that the sun was shining, remembered it wasn't wash day anyway, and came back to find the cameras showing the layout of the course. First there was a shot of a huge pillar of stone, the height of a man, standing upright in the ground.

"Today is the day"

"Here," said the voice of the commentator, "is where each handler will stand, and from here each dog will start his outrun; he can go left or right, to get into position behind his sheep; today each dog will have ten sheep to work; they will be grouped near that distant post, called the Holding Post" (all the time the cameras followed his explanations), "and then he must fetch his sheep, through the Fetch Gates, all the way back to the Handler's Post, and round it; then the dog drives the sheep away—to the left as we look at it—through the Drive Away Gates, turns them right again and straight across the line of his fetch, through the Cross Drive Gates, and right again to the Shedding Ring, and when he's shed his sheep and collected them again, then finally he must pen them here."

"Mouthy old thing!" said Mrs. Hogget, turning the sound off. "Some folk never know how to hold their tongues, keeping on and on about them silly gates, why don't 'e show us a picture of the spectators, might catch a glimpse of Hogget and Fly, you never knows, though not the pig, I hopes, he's surely not daft enough to walk about with the pig, can't see why he wanted to take un all that way just to lie in the back of the Land Rover, he'd have done better to leave un here and let un sit and watch it on the telly in comfort

103

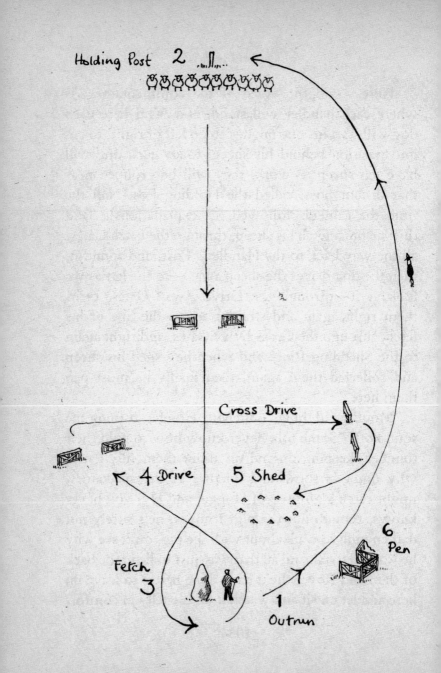

Holding Post 2

Cross Drive

4 Drive

5 Shed

6 Pen

Fetch
3

1
Outrun

which is more than some of us have got time for, I got work to do," and she stumped off into the kitchen, shaking her head madly.

On the silent screen the first handler walked out and took up his position beside the great sarsen stone, his dog standing by him, tense and eager in the pouring rain.

CHAPTER 12

"That'll do"

Hundreds of thousands of pairs of eyes watched that first dog, but none more keenly than those of Hogget, Fly, and Babe.

The car-park was a big sloping field overlooking the course, and the farmer had driven the Land Rover to the topmost corner, well away from other cars. From inside, the three so different faces watched intently.

Conditions, Hogget could see immediately, were very difficult. In addition to the driving rain, which made the going slippery and the sheep more obstinate than usual, there was quite a strong wind blowing almost directly from the Holding Post back toward the handler, and the dog was finding it hard to hear commands.

The more anxious the dog was, the more the sheep

tried to break from him, and thus the angrier he became. It was a vicious circle, and when at last the ten sheep were penned and the handler pulled the gate shut and cried "That'll do!" no one was surprised that they had scored no more than seventy points out of a possible hundred.

So it went on. Man after man came to stand beside the great sarsen stone, men from the North and from the West, from Scotland, and Wales, and Ireland, with dogs and bitches, large and small, rough-coated and smooth, black-and-white or gray or brown or blue merle. Some fared better than others of course, were steadier on their sheep or had steadier sheep to deal with. But still, as Farmer Hogget's turn drew near (as luck would have it, he was last to go), there was no score higher than eighty-five.

At home Mrs. Hogget chanced to turn the sound of the television back up in time to hear the commentator confirm this.

"One more to go," he said, "and the target to beat is eighty-five points, set by Mr. Jones from Wales and his dog Bryn, a very creditable total considering the appalling weather conditions we have up here today. It's very hard to imagine that score being beaten, but here comes the last competitor to try and do just that," and suddenly there appeared on the screen before Mrs. Hogget's eyes the tall long-striding figure of her husband, walking out toward the great stone with tubby old Fly at his heels.

"This is Mr. Hogget with Pig," said the commentator. "A bit of a strange name that, but then I must say his dog's rather on the fat side . . . hullo, he's sending the dog back . . . what on earth? . . . oh, good heavens! . . . Will you look at that!"

And as Mrs. Hogget and hundreds of thousands of other viewers looked, they saw Fly go trotting back toward the car-park.

And from it, cantering through the continuing rain, came the long, lean, beautifully clean figure of a Large White pig.

Straight to Hogget's side ran Babe, and stood like a statue, his great ears fanned, his little eyes fixed upon the distant sheep.

At home, Mrs. Hogget's mouth opened wide, but for once no sound came from it.

On the course, there was a moment of stunned silence and then a great burst of noise.

On the screen, the cameras showed every aspect of the amazing scene—the spectators pointing, gaping, grinning; the red-faced judges hastily conferring; Hogget and Babe waiting patiently; and finally the commentator.

"This is really quite ridiculous," he said with a shamefaced smile, "but in point of fact there seems to be nothing in the rule book that says that only sheepdogs may compete. So it looks as though the judges are bound to allow Mr. Hogget to run this, er, sheep-pig I suppose we'll have to call it, ha, ha! One look at it, and the sheep will disappear into the next county without a doubt! Still, we might as well end the day with a good laugh!"

And indeed at that moment a great gale of laughter arose, as Hogget, receiving a most unwilling nod from the judges, said quietly, "Away to me, Pig," and Babe began his outrun to the right.

How they roared at the mere sight of him running (though many noticed how fast he went), and at the purely crazy thought of a pig herding sheep, and especially at the way he squealed and squealed at the top of his voice, in foolish excitement they supposed.

But though he was excited, tremendously excited at the thrill of actually competing in the Grand

Challenge Sheepdog Trials, Babe was nobody's fool. He was yelling out the password: "I may be ewe, I may be ram, I may be mutton, may be lamb, but on the hoof or on the hook, I bain't so stupid as I look," as he ran.

This was the danger point—before he'd met his sheep—and again and again he repeated the magic words, shouting above the noise of wind and rain, his eyes fixed on the ten sheep by the Holding Post. Their eyes were just as fixed on him, eyes that bulged at the sight of this great strange animal approaching, but they held steady, and the now distant crowd fell suddenly silent as they saw the pig take up a perfect

111

position behind his sheep, and heard the astonished judges award ten points for a faultless outrun.

Just for luck, in case they hadn't believed their ears, Babe gave the password one last time. ". . . I bain't so stupid as I look," he panted, "and a very good afternoon to you all, and I do apologize for having to ask you to work in this miserable weather, I hope you'll forgive me?"

At once, as he had hoped, there was a positive babble of voices.

"Fancy him knowing the pa-a-a-a-a-assword!"

"What lovely ma-a-a-a-anners!"

"Not like them na-a-a-a-asty wolves!"

"What d'you want us to do, young ma-a-a-a-aster?"

Quickly, for he was conscious that time was ticking away, Babe, first asking politely for their attention, outlined the course to them.

"And I would be really most awfully grateful," he said, "if you would all bear these points in mind. Keep tightly together, go at a good steady pace, not too fast, not too slow, and walk exactly through the middle of each of the three gates, if you'd be good enough. The moment I enter the shedding ring, would the four of you who are wearing collars (how nice they look, by the way) please walk out of it. And then if you'd all kindly go straight into the final pen, I should be so much obliged."

All this talk took quite a time, and the crowd and the judges and Mrs. Hogget and her hundreds of thousands of fellow-viewers began to feel that nothing else was going to happen, that the sheep were never going to move, that the whole thing was a stupid farce, a silly joke that had fallen flat.

Only Hogget, standing silent in the rain beside the sarsen stone, had complete confidence in the skills of the sheep-pig.

And suddenly the miracle began to happen.

Marching two by two, as steady as guardsmen on parade, the ten sheep set off for the Fetch Gates, Babe a few paces behind them, silent, powerful, confident. Straight as a die they went toward the distant Hogget, straight between the exact center of the Fetch Gates, without a moment's hesitation, without deviating an inch from their unswerving course. Hogget said nothing, made no sign, gave no whistle, did not move as the sheep rounded him so closely as almost to brush his boots, and, the Fetch completed, set off for the Drive Away Gates. Once again, their pace never changing, looking neither to left nor to right, keeping so tight a formation that you could have dropped a big tablecloth over the lot, they passed through the precise middle of the Drive Away Gates, and turned as one animal to face the Cross Drive Gates.

It was just the same here. The sheep passed through perfectly and wheeled for the Shedding Ring, while all the time the judges' scorecards showed maximum points and the crowd watched in a kind of hypnotized hush, whispering to one another for fear of breaking the spell.

"He's not put a foot wrong!"

"Bang through the middle of every gate."

"Lovely steady pace."

"And the handler, he's not said a word, not even

114

moved, just stood there leaning on his stick."

"Ah, but he'll have to move now—you're never going to tell me that pig can shed four sheep out of the ten on his own!"

The Shedding Ring was a circle perhaps forty yards in diameter, marked out by little heaps of sawdust, and into it the sheep walked, still calm, still collected, and stood waiting.

Outside the circle Babe waited, his eyes on Hogget.

The crowd waited.

Mrs. Hogget waited.

Hundreds of thousands of viewers waited.

Then, just as it seemed nothing more would happen, that the man had somehow lost control of the sheep-pig, that the sheep-pig had lost interest in his sheep, Farmer Hogget raised his stick and with it gave one sharp tap upon the great sarsen stone, a tap that sounded like a pistol shot in the tense atmosphere.

And at this signal Babe walked gently into the circle and up to his sheep.

"Beautifully done," he said to them quietly, "I can't tell you how grateful I am to you all. Now, if the four ladies with collars would kindly walk out of the ring when I give a grunt, I should be so much obliged. Then if you would all be good enough to wait until my boss has walked across to the final collecting pen over there and opened its gate, all that remains for you to do is to pop in. Would you do that? Please?"

"A-a-a-a-a-a-ar," they said softly, and as Babe gave one deep grunt the four collared sheep detached themselves from their companions and calmly, unhurriedly, walked out of the Shedding Ring.

Unmoving, held by the magic of the moment, the crowd watched with no sound but a great sigh of amazement. No one could quite believe his eyes. No one seemed to notice that the wind had dropped and the rain had stopped. No one was surprised when a single shaft of sunshine came suddenly through a hole in the gray clouds and shone full upon the great sarsen stone. Slowly, with his long strides, Hogget left it and walked to the little enclosure of hurdles, the final test of his shepherding. He opened its gate and stood, silent still, while the shed animals walked back into the ring to rejoin the rest.

Then he nodded once at Babe, no more, and steadily, smartly, straightly, the ten sheep, with the sheep-pig at their heels, marched into the final pen, and Hogget closed the gate.

As he dropped the loop of rope over the hurdle stake, everyone could see the judges' marks.

A hundred out of a hundred, the perfect perform-ance, never before reached by man and dog in the whole history of sheepdog trials, but now achieved by man and pig, and everyone went mad!

At home Mrs. Hogget erupted, like a volcano, into a great lava flow of words, pouring them out toward the two figures held by the camera, as though they were actually inside that box in the corner of her sitting room, cheering them, praising them, congratulating first one and then the other, telling them how proud she was, to hurry home, not to be late for supper, it was shepherd's pie.

As for the crowd of spectators at the Grand Challenge Sheepdog Trials they shouted and yelled and waved their arms and jumped about, while the astonished judges scratched their heads and the amazed competitors shook theirs in wondering disbelief.

"Marvelous! Ma-a-a-a-a-arvelous!" bleated the ten penned sheep. And from the back of an ancient Land Rover at the top of the car-park a tubby old black-and-white collie bitch, her plumed tail wagging wildly, barked and barked and barked for joy.

In all the hubbub of noise and excitement, two figures still stood silently side by side.

Then Hogget bent, and gently scratching Babe between his great ears, uttered those words that every handler always says to his working companion when the job is finally done.

Perhaps no one else heard the words, but if they did, there was no doubting the truth of them.

"That'll do," said Farmer Hogget to his sheep-pig. "That'll do."

DICK KING-SMITH was born and raised in Gloucestershire, England. After twenty years as a farmer, he turned to teaching and then to writing the children's books that have earned him critical acclaim on both sides of the Atlantic. *Babe: The Gallant Pig*, one of his best-loved books, was made into a major motion picture. His other award-winning titles include *Ace: The Very Important Pig*, *Three Terrible Trins*, and *Martin's Mice*.

ACE:
The Very Important Pig

by Dick King-Smith

A ce is no ordinary pig. He understands human language completely, and he's determined to avoid the awful fate that befalls his brothers and sisters: the Market. First, he befriends the farmer's house pets, easygoing Clarence the cat and Megan, the snobby corgi. Next, he works his way into Farmer Tubbs's heart and home—and even into the farmer's favorite armchair! But it's not until Tubbs takes him to town that Ace finds fame beyond his wildest dreams...

★ "While E. B. White's Wilbur will long endure in our hearts...Ace may run him some pretty stiff competition."
—*The Horn Book* (starred review)

★ "Ace is an intelligent, lovable, unlikely pig hero."
—*School Library Journal* (starred review)

"This winsome story is sure to warm hearts and bring smiles."
—*Publishers Weekly*

An IRA-CBC Children's Choice
A *School Library Journal* Best Book of the Year
A *Horn Book* Fanfare Honor Book

A KNOPF PAPERBACK PUBLISHED BY ALFRED A. KNOPF

Three Terrible Trins

by Dick King-Smith

The terrible trins (like twins, but three) are a fearsome lot. These three mice are about to turn things upside down at Orchard Farm—and teach the farmer's cats who's really boss. But outwitting bad-tempered Farmer Budge and his pesky mousetraps isn't going to be quite so easy. It'll take some fancy footwork and the help of all four mouse clans to make things safe at Orchard Farm once and for all.

★"All in all, a delightful romp."
—*School Library Journal* (starred review)

★"A deftly written, fast-paced animal fantasy."
—*Booklist* (starred review)

"King-Smith grabs the reader's attention from his opening sentence. And...the author never loosens his grip."
—*Publishers Weekly*

An ALA Notable Book
An IRA-CBC Children's Choice
A *Booklist* Editors' Choice

A KNOPF PAPERBACK PUBLISHED BY ALFRED A. KNOPF

Harriet's Hare

by Dick King-Smith

The last thing Harriet Butler expects to meet is a talking hare from outer space. But one morning, in her father's wheat field, that's exactly what happens. Wiz (as Harriet names him) turns out to be a master of surprises and the best friend she's had since her mother died. She comes to dread the day he'll return to his own planet, leaving her even lonelier than before.

But Wiz has more in store for Harriet than she could ever imagine. And before he goes, he'll give Harriet a gift that is sure to change her life...forever.

"A warm tale full of gentle poignance, frolicking humor, and magic...Those who have yet to discover this talented author should be charmed."
—*School Library Journal*

★"A tender, heartwarming story...Children will find themselves completely drawn into [the] wonderful fantasy adventures."
—*Booklist* (starred review)

A KNOPF PAPERBACK PUBLISHED BY ALFRED A. KNOPF

The Invisible Dog

by Dick King-Smith

Henry is Janie's new dog, a magnificent Great Dane with big black spots. The only unusual thing about Henry is that Janie can't see him. In fact, no one can—he's invisible!

But everyone agrees that Henry makes the perfect pet. He's always quiet and obedient. He even eats invisible food bought with invisible money! Still, Janie can't help wishing that her pretend Great Dane was a little more real. Then a chain of mysterious events—and perhaps a touch of magic—bring the invisible Henry to life!

"King-Smith has created another irresistible yarn...that readers will love."   —*Booklist*

"...chock full of warmth, zany imagination and soft-hearted irony. This novel will appeal to animal lovers of all ages."
                                                                —*Publishers Weekly*

A KNOPF PAPERBACK PUBLISHED BY ALFRED A. KNOPF